Dear Ken,

What's for Dinner? is definitely not your average cooking show and that's what makes it so fun to watch … the good-natured joking around reminds me of cooking with my friends.

Your recipes are innovative and easy to prepare, which I like. In fact, watching your show started me cooking and eating healthier. If you have done any low-fat dessert recipes, or are planning to in the future, I would really love to get copies of these.

Sincerely,

Chris in Stoney Creek, Ontario

What's For
Dinner?
Cooks Low Fat

What's For Dinner?

Cooks Low Fat

Ken Kostick

In cooperation with the YMCA

MACMILLAN CANADA
TORONTO

Canadian Cataloguing in Publication Data

Kostick, Ken, 1954-
    What's for dinner? cooks low fat

Includes index.
ISBN 0-7715-7596-3

1. Low-fat diet – Recipes. I Title.
RM237.7.K67 1999   641.5'638   C98-932510-5

This book is available at special discounts for bulk purchases by your group or organization for sales promotions, premiums, fundraising and seminars. For details, contact: Macmillan Canada, Special Sales Department, 29 Birch Avenue, Toronto, ON, M4V 1E2. Tel: 416-963-8830.

Cover and book design: Sharon Foster Design
Photos on front and back cover and on p. i and p. 178: Tim Leyes

We acknowledge the financial support of the Government of Canada through the Book Publishing Industry Development Program for our publishing activities.

Macmillan Canada
A Division of Canada Publishing Corporation
Toronto, Ontario, Canada

1 2 3 4 5   TRI   03 02 01 00 99

Printed in Canada

I would like to dedicate this book to
Jamie, Pearl and Benny.
You make each day a wonderful day.

Ruby, my other boxer, passed away
peacefully in August 1997.

Acknowledgements

The following friends and colleagues have been very important in the creation of this book. I would not have been able to do this without the support and friendship that I have received. Thank you.

Nicole de Montbrun—my editor and friend, at Macmillan Canada. This woman should be given an award for her professionalism and patience. She is one lovely woman. Thank you for your guidance and constant encouragement.

Gill Humphreys—my next-door neighbour, best friend and confidante. We sit on my porch and solve all the problems of the world as well as adding a bit of humour to our already-interesting lives. Thank you for being best buds.

Donald Martin—thank you for your continuous humour and support. I have never known anyone like you—*everything* seems to happen to you. And you are not only a good and devoted friend but also a secret comedian.

Mary Jo, please note that I have spelled your name correctly—thank you for your daily sense of humour and for being such a good friend. When I needed support you were there and I will never forget that. Thank you.

Robert Townsend, travel agent and friend—thank you for all your help. Your professionalism made my job so much easier when travelling. Over the past two years you have become a good friend. Thank you.

The Television Crew—I cannot express how enjoyable it is going to working with such a great crew. This crew makes Mary Jo and me look good every day. I can't thank you enough.

Macmillan Canada, Alison, Meghan and everyone—thank you so much for your belief in me and in this book.

Friendly Kitchen Company—thank you Ira, Peter, Deb, Sarah and Lindsay for your support in the television series and this book.

Celebrity Events, Lilana, Kathy and Laurie—thank you so much for your support and making my public appearances so much fun.

Life Network—without the television series there would not be a book. To everyone involved: thank you for having the confidence in "What's For Dinner?" and in this book. Your efforts are much appreciated.

My friends Rob, Barry, Brian, Jason, Nancy, Doug, Channing, Andy, Georgette, Anne, Pauline, Steve, Marie, Hal and Rae—each of you has given me much support for this book. Thank you all!

Helen Kostick, my mom and, yes, the person who taught me everything I know about cooking (her words)—thank you for your help on this book and for just being Mom. Love ya!

Letter from the YMCA

Ken Kostick, his publishers, and the YMCA have combined their talents to create something quite special: a book that will satisfy your hunger for flavourful, nutritious meals and guide you to a more active lifestyle.

We are proud that Ken is one of the 1.3 million Canadians who turn to the YMCA for support through our many different programs. In over 200 communities, the YMCA is a part of their daily routine. Everyday we help people maintain good health or recover from injury or illness. We care for children and teach them physical and social skills. We work with youth to uncover their talents for leadership. We accompany people through their employment transitions. We cultivate community leaders. We provide a place for people from all backgrounds and circumstances to come together and share experiences. In so doing, we are building stronger communities.

We hope that this book will become a part of your every day; a faithful "dog-eared, spatula-stained" kitchen companion. The food and fitness guides are guaranteed to lead you to better health. It is also our hope that this book will lead you to connect with others who seek greater vitality. As Ken discovered so many years ago, the opportunities to study, play, work and serve alongside others are plentiful. All are welcome. Look into what's happening at your neighbourhood YMCA, where together people grow in spirit, mind and body.

Through this cookbook, many more people will be able to have the kinds of experiences that Ken has had through the YMCA. We thank him for his example and for sharing the wisdom that he has gained on his journey thus far.

The YMCA in Canada

Dear Ken,

I absolutely love your show—it's the best cooking show on TV. Your constant banter and teasing are hilarious. Your recipes are all quick, easy, and nutritious and I always have the ingredients in my fridge or pantry.

Thanks,
Barbara in St. Albert, Alberta

CONTENTS

Introduction

One morning, in January 1993, I decided to change some things in my life. That day, as I struggled to put on my shoes, I realized that my eating habits were putting my health at risk.

The problem, of course, was my love of food—all food. I regularly indulged in fried foods and junk foods. As I considered my diet, my lack of exercise, and the fact that I was nearing my fortieth birthday, I knew that I had to alter my habits. And this time it was going to be for good.

Celebrating my new-found conviction that night, I prepared a "last supper." Fried chicken, mashed potatoes and dessert were on the menu. The very next morning, I cleaned out my kitchen—a very important first step. Out went pastries, candy, soft drinks, processed food, and snack foods. These were replaced with fruits, vegetables, fresh and dried herbs, poultry, fish, and meat.

I also tossed out the salt! This was especially hard to do since I sprinkled salt on everything. Instead, I would begin flavouring my food with a concoction of dried herbs: basil, oregano, pepper, paprika and just a dash of cayenne to give it a kick.

Once my kitchen was in order, I researched the fat and calorie content of foods. With that valuable information, I could make important decisions as to how much of what I should eat on a daily basis.

I next turned my attention to my exercise program. Years earlier, I had trained in jujitsu—for almost 10 years, actually—and I briefly considered the benefits of, once again, being regularly thrown across a room. I chose running, instead.

On that first, cold January morning, I bundled up and set out to run a mile. I got as far as two blocks. Surprisingly, I wasn't discouraged, just happy to get home. I remember thinking: "Okay, two blocks today, but tomorrow and each day I run, I will extend my running a bit farther." I was resolved to improve, but also determined not to impose any kind of deadline. My health was the most important concern: weight loss was a factor too, but it had to be a gradual weight loss.

Any previous diet and exercise regimen I had undergone had come with strict goals and impossible schedules—this time I would do it right. This was not a diet but a new way of living: this was not to last a month, six months or a year, but a lifetime. I would change the way I viewed food and exercise and fit this into my very busy lifestyle.

Since that January, I have lost a total of 55 pounds. I accomplished this loss gradually, over a two-year period *and* with the combination of exercise and healthy eating. Yet, during those years, I occasionally indulged in a cheeseburger and fries, or a piece of chocolate cake. I still do, just not every day. I have learned that it is important to reward myself. In the past, whenever I followed a very restrictive diet, I soon craved fattening foods. I couldn't wait to lose the weight so that I could resume my old eating habits. Once I did, of course, the weight came back with a vengeance.

I rarely crave those foods now because I've learned how to cook low-fat, healthy food that tastes delicious—I never feel like I'm depriving myself.

To keep myself on track, each week I carefully plan what I'm going to buy. When I dine in a restaurant, I always request that my food be prepared a certain way (grilled, broiled, or poached) or without sauces that I know will add too much fat. I try to exercise every other day; a combination of running, weights and a punching bag (good for stress). I do all of this at my local YMCA; or at the one closest to where I'm staying when travelling.

The low-fat recipes in this cookbook (all of which I've developed since 1993), are designed to inspire you. As are the YMCA's fitness tips that accompany many of these recipes. Try some of these suggestions and have fun with your new attitude towards food and exercise.

The YMCA

I was raised in a loving family, surrounded by parents, a sister and numerous foster siblings. Although my parents didn't have money for extras, it scarcely mattered because we had our local YMCA. Then, as now, we could choose from a wide array of programs for children, teens, adults and seniors. It was our community centre, and we were always welcome.

Many years later, I'm still a regular at the YMCA: at home or across the country when I travel. The facilities, equipment and services provided are state of the art, as is the staff, who are on hand to offer advice or assistance.

The YMCA continues to have programs for people of all ages and all income levels. During my weekly visits, I'm always struck by the diversity of its membership, and especially by the numbers of families who continue to attend.

That's why I'm a supporter of the YMCA—it ensures a better quality of life for everyone.

Shopping List

On the first day of your brand new life, completely clean out the kitchen. Junk the processed food, prepared desserts, candy, ice cream, fried foods—and any potential items for frying foods (large containers of oil)—and any perogies you may have in your freezer (Mom, they went to friends!). Leave nothing that will tempt you. Instead, stock the fridge and pantry with the type of foods listed below that will help you maintain a new and healthy attitude towards food.

Spray Oils, Canola Oil, and Olive Oil

Low-Fat Canned Soup Stocks—I always have on hand vegetable, chicken, onion and beef stock.

Unsweetened Juices—use these for sautéing and adding flavour to marinades and sauces.

Vinegars—apple cider, rice wine, balsamic and other flavoured vinegars: these are great for seasoning.

Dried Herbs and Spices—adding these to food replaces the need for salt. (My shelves are stocked with basil, oregano, thyme, chili powder, curry powder, cayenne, garlic powder, onion powder, combination herbs and spices, sea salt, black pepper and white pepper)

Canned Goods—such as canned tomatoes and canned beans, as well as canned or bottled tomato sauce and salsa. (Please check the label to make sure these do not contain a high volume of sodium.)

Pasta—try an assortment of shapes and types including rice pasta, as well as pasta made from non-wheat products such as soya, rice and spelt. Also try vermicelli and low-fat egg noodles.

Rice—you can never have too much rice in the cupboard, and why limit yourself to white rice when there's basmati, brown, wild and fragant rice.

Vegetables—always buy a varied selection of fresh vegetables. The trick is not to buy too much of one kind of vegetable. For convenience, I buy frozen vegetables.

Fruit—as with vegetables, don't purchase too much of any one kind of fruit. Buy a selection to give you variety in your new eating plan. Cut up fruit and keep in plastic containers in the fridge so that an easy snack will be a fruit salad in its own juices.

Meat—all the meat I buy is very lean and, if it needs to be trimmed of any excess fat, I do this prior to cooking. Because I have meat 2 to 3 times a week, I limit myself to 4 to 6 ounces per serving.

Poultry—chicken and turkey are regulars at my house. I prepare the chicken breasts without the skin and make sure that I do the same with turkey. These are flavourful and healthy. Poach, grill or roast the above to ensure low-fat preparation.

Fish—I always bake, grill or poach fish. The trick here is to have fish at least once or twice a week and try different types you can get at the local supermarket. Cod, sole, red snapper, swordfish and trout. The use of dried herbs is essential in the preparation and you will become thrilled with your seafood friend. Buy fresh or frozen but just enough for that week.

30-day Menu Plan

In order to maintain a consistent weight loss, I had 3 well-balanced meals a day as well as 2 to 3 snacks. Whenever I missed breakfast or skipped lunch, my energy level waned and my appetite increased so that I was tempted to overeat, and to eat the wrong kinds of food.

Below, I have prepared a menu plan that you can follow. Use this as a guide, but remember to treat yourself once a week with something you really desire.

BREAKFAST

A good breakfast should consist of 1 or 2 of the following: a low-fat cereal with skim milk, toast, toasted whole-grain bagel, assortment of fruit, yogurt, 2 poached eggs, 2 scrambled eggs or omelet with vegetables. Occasionally have some bacon or sausages. Try some turkey bacon, which has less fat and sodium than regular bacon. On occasion, treat yourself to a pancake topped with fruit and yogurt or French toast with pure fruit jam.

LUNCH

The following are great suggestions for lunch: soup (not the cream-based kind) and salad. Or an open-face sandwich or slice of pizza. Or a small portion of pasta with a tomato sauce. Or a vegetable stir-fry (try different versions). Or a small portion (4 oz) of grilled fish, poultry or beef, served with a salad.

For snacks, choose fruit, fruit and more fruit: 1 apple, banana, peach or orange. Or indulge in carrots and celery once a day. I would recommend a fruit snack around 10:00 or 11:00 and another snack around 3:00 or 4:00 p.m.

Occasionally (once a week) treat yourself with something you really want in a snack. You need to be good to yourself.

* Use a little butter on toast or bagels.

* Do not use heavy salad dressing on salads (lemon oil, oil and vinegar and fruit juice).

* Stir-fries—small amount of oil or stir-fry in soup stocks (low fat) or fruit juices.

* Sandwiches—limit mayonnaise and other dressings.

* Pizzas—try vegetarian pizza and limit the amount of cheese.

* Salt—reduce salt intake on all above.

* If eating out—request the above and usually they will accommodate.

30-day Menu Plan

DAY 1	DAY 2	DAY 3	DAY 4	DAY 5	DAY 6
Breakfast Toast & Poached Egg **Lunch** Soup & Salad **Dinner** Tri-colour Fusilli with Goat cheese	**Breakfast** Fruit & Yogurt **Lunch** Pasta in Tomato Sauce **Dinner** Grilled Lemon Chicken with Rosemary	**Breakfast** Bagel & Scrambled Egg **Lunch** Vegetable Stir-Fry **Dinner** Shrimp and Fennel Salad	**Breakfast** Cereal & Fruit **Lunch** Small Pizza **Dinner** Sesame Grilled Steak and Bean Salad	**Breakfast** French Toast **Lunch** Fish & Salad **Dinner** Mushroom Bow-Tie Pasta	**Breakfast** Bagel & Fruit **Lunch** Soup & Salad **Dinner** Chili Ratatouille

DAY 7	DAY 8	DAY 9	DAY 10	DAY 11	DAY 12
Breakfast Plain Omelet & Toast **Lunch** Salad & Small Pizza **Dinner** Herb Chicken with Roasted Almonds	**Breakfast** Fruit & Toast **Lunch** Soup & Salad **Dinner** Stir-Fried Beef with Ginger	**Breakfast** Bacon & Toast **Lunch** Sandwich & Salad **Dinner** Vegetarian Cabbage Rolls	**Breakfast** Cereal & Fruit **Lunch** Chicken & Salad **Dinner** Scallops with Tomatoes & Zucchini	**Breakfast** Pancakes **Lunch** Vegetable Stir-Fry **Dinner** Stuffed Turkey Bundles in Tomato Sauce	**Breakfast** Fruit & Yogurt **Lunch** Soup & Sandwich **Dinner** Garlic Beef Tenderloin

DAY 13	DAY 14	DAY 15	DAY 16	DAY 17	DAY 18
Breakfast Cereal & Toast **Lunch** Pasta & Salad **Dinner** Tomato Beef Stew	**Breakfast** Poach Eggs & Toast **Lunch** Soup & Salad **Dinner** Penne with Roasted Vegetables	**Breakfast** Bagel & Yogurt **Lunch** Soup & Sandwich **Dinner** Pork Chops with Lemon and Sage	**Breakfast** Fruit & Toast **Lunch** Vegetable Stir-Fry **Dinner** Garlic-Roasted Chicken and Fennel	**Breakfast** Sausages & Eggs **Lunch** Grilled Beef & Salad **Dinner** Mushroom & Herb Risotto	**Breakfast** Fruit & Toast **Lunch** Pizza & Salad **Dinner** Baked Turkey with Pineapple Salsa

DAY 19	DAY 20	DAY 21	DAY 22	DAY 23	DAY 24
Breakfast Cereal & Fruit **Lunch** Vegetable Stir-Fry **Dinner** Orange and Garlic Lamb Chops	**Breakfast** Toast & Fruit **Lunch** Grilled Chicken & Salad **Dinner** Minty Seafood Rice Medley	**Breakfast** Poached Egg & Bagel **Lunch** Soup & Salad **Dinner** Vegetable Herb Lasagna	**Breakfast** Fruit & Toast **Lunch** Pizza & Soup **Dinner** Sweet Red Peppers and Chicken	**Breakfast** Pancakes **Lunch** Soup & Sandwich **Dinner** Mediterranean Lamb Stew	**Breakfast** Eggs & Sausage **Lunch** Fish & Salad **Dinner** Spicy Vegetarian Paella

DAY 25	DAY 26	DAY 27	DAY 28	DAY 29	DAY 30
Breakfast Bagel & Fruit **Lunch** Vegetable Stir-Fry **Dinner** Stuffed Chicken Breasts	**Breakfast** Fruit & Yogurt **Lunch** Pizza & Salad **Dinner** Crabmeat-Stuffed Cod	**Breakfast** Scrambled Egg & Toast **Lunch** Soup & Salad **Dinner** Grilled New York Steak	**Breakfast** Cereal & Fruit **Lunch** Grilled Chicken & Salad **Dinner** Vegetable Risotto	**Breakfast** French Toast **Lunch** Sandwich & Salad **Dinner** Ken's Favourite Fish Stew	**Breakfast** Omelet & Bagel **Lunch** Pasta & Salad **Dinner** Baked Chicken with Grapefruit

Dear Ken,

A month ago, I tuned into What's for Dinner? for the first time. It is THE BEST cooking program I've ever seen—and I've seen plenty! Not just because the meals are cooked in a half hour, but because the meals are good and nutritious.

Many thanks and continue cooking good meals!
Shirley in Bermuda

SOUPS

Chilled Borscht

SERVES 8

CALORIES PER SERVING: 80.9

FAT (G) PER SERVING: 0.7

This is my version of an old favourite.

2 14-oz cans beets, drained
1 small onion, chopped
1 clove garlic
4 cups vegetable stock (low-sodium/low-fat)

2 cups non-fat sour cream
1/2 cup chopped fresh dill
1/2 tsp black pepper
1/2 tsp dried basil

In a food processor, combine beets, onion, garlic, stock, sour cream, dill, pepper and basil; purée until nice and smooth. Chill in the refrigerator for at least 1 hour before serving.

Substitution:
• *Substitute parsley for dill.*

Vegetarian Substitution:
• *Substitute rice or soy milk or sour cream for the sour cream.*

Gazpacho Soup

SERVES 6

CALORIES PER SERVING: 100.6

FAT (G) PER SERVING: 1.1

Gazpacho soup on a hot summer's day is my idea of heaven. The recipe allows you to use the fresh vegetables in season—plum tomatoes, red and green peppers and cucumber. Serve cold as a starter with something grilled or as a whole meal with a salad.

1 28-oz can stewed tomatoes, chopped

4 medium plum tomatoes, chopped

2 celery stalks, chopped

1 red pepper, chopped

1 green pepper, chopped

1 small cucumber, diced

1 small onion, chopped

4 cups vegetable stock (low-sodium/low-fat)

2 cups tomato juice

2 tbsp chopped fresh basil

1 tbsp chopped fresh dill

1 tsp chili powder

1/2 tsp black pepper

1/2 tsp salt

2 tbsp wine vinegar

In a large bowl, combine tomatoes, celery, peppers, cucumber, onion, stock, tomato juice, basil, dill, chili powder, black pepper, salt and vinegar. Refrigerate for at least 1 hour before serving. Serve cold in soup bowls.

Your body fat increases by 1% to 2% per decade, which means that for each year over age 30, you need about 10 to 15 fewer calories a day to maintain your weight.

Substitution:
• Substitute fresh coriander for the dill.

Another Gazpacho Soup

SERVES 6

CALORIES PER SERVING: 102.4

FAT (G) PER SERVING: 0.9

While writing this book at my log cabin, I served this soup to some company. A friend of mine ate the whole batch in two sittings—on Friday for dinner and on Saturday for lunch. I guess it was a hit.

4 cups vegetable stock (low-sodium/low-fat)
1 small zucchini, diced
2 celery stalks, chopped
8 asparagus stalks, chopped
1 small cucumber, diced
1 onion, chopped
1 large carrot, grated
2 cloves garlic, chopped
1 red pepper, chopped
1 green pepper, chopped
1 tsp finely chopped jalapeño pepper
1/2 cup chopped fresh coriander
1/2 cup chopped fresh parsley
1 tbsp chopped fresh basil
2 tbsp lemon juice
2 tbsp balsamic vinegar
2 cups tomato juice
1 28-oz can stewed tomatoes

In a large soup pot, bring 2 cups of the stock to a boil. Gently blanch the zucchini, celery and asparagus about 2 minutes. Remove from the heat. Remove the vegetables and allow to cool. Reserve the stock. Return the cooled blanched vegetables to the stock and toss in the cucumber, onion, carrot, garlic, peppers, coriander, parsley, basil, lemon juice, vinegar, tomato juice and tomatoes. Mix well. Place in the fridge to cool at least 1 hour before serving. Serve cool, not ice cold, and garnish with fresh parsley. If the soup is too thick, add more tomato juice, but keep in mind that this soup is like a fresh salad and should be quite chunky.

Strength training and aerobic workouts are crucial for middle-aged men and women as bone density starts declining for those over 50.

Substitution:
• *Substitute fresh mint or dill with the coriander.*

Chilled Cucumber Soup with Mint

SERVES 6

CALORIES PER SERVING: 86.3

FAT (G) PER SERVING: 0.4

If you want the taste of summer all year long, try this cucumber soup.

2 large cucumbers, peeled and chopped
1 small onion, chopped
1 clove garlic, chopped
3 cups non-fat plain yogurt
2 tbsp lemon juice

2 cups vegetable stock (low-sodium/low-fat)
1 tbsp balsamic vinegar
1/2 tsp black pepper
1/2 cup chopped fresh mint

In a blender or food processor, toss the cucumbers, onion, garlic, yogurt, lemon juice, stock, vinegar, pepper and 1/4 cup mint. Purée until smooth. Chill in the refrigerator at least 1 hour before serving. Garnish with fresh mint and diced cucumber.

It is never too late to switch to a low-fat, high-fibre diet, which can help prevent the risk of heart disease, stroke and cancers of the colon, rectum and prostate.

Substitution:
• Substitute fresh parsley for the mint.

Vegetarian Substitution:
• Substitute the yogurt with rice or soy milk or sour cream.

Honeydew Melon Soup

SERVES 4

CALORIES PER SERVING: 175.4

FAT (G) PER SERVING: < 0.5

Cold soup is popular in France, Spain and Greece.

1 large honeydew melon, diced
2 cups unsweetened apple juice
1 cup non-fat yogurt
2 tbsp lemon juice

1/4 cup finely chopped fresh mint
1/4 tsp cinnamon
1 tbsp finely chopped fresh
   parsley

In a food processor or blender, combine the melon, apple juice, yogurt, lemon juice, mint and cinnamon. Purée until smooth. Chill in the refrigerator to allow flavours to blend together. Garnish with parsley.

Women in their forties should be sure to get enough calcium. Calcium and strength training can help guard against osteoporosis.

Substitution:
• *Replace melon with other fruit such as strawberries, pear or peach. If you do, replace the apple juice with a pear or peach juice.*

Vegetarian Substitution:
• *Substitute the yogurt with soy or rice milk or low-fat soy or rice sour cream.*

Creamy Spinach Soup with Fennel

SERVES 6 TO 8

CALORIES PER SERVING: 74.5

FAT (G) PER SERVING: 0.7

Soup, soup and more soup. I seem to want to make and eat soup all the time. I like the idea that in some cultures soup is eaten at breakfast. Spinach and nutmeg make a wonderful combination in this soup.

6 cups vegetable stock (low-sodium/low-fat)
1 medium onion, chopped
1 fennel bulb, chopped
2 medium potatoes, cubed
8 cups spinach, chopped
1/2 tsp dried basil
1/2 tsp dried mint
1/2 tsp dried oregano
1/4 tsp ground nutmeg
1/2 tsp black pepper
1 bay leaf
1 cup non-fat yogurt

In a large soup pot, heat 1/2 cup of the stock and sauté the onion, fennel and potatoes 4 minutes or until vegetables are tender. Add the remaining stock, spinach, basil, mint, oregano, nutmeg, pepper and bay leaf. Bring to a boil and reduce to a simmer for about 20 minutes. If the soup reduces too much, just add more stock. Remove the bay leaf. Add yogurt and, using a hand blender, blend the soup until it has a creamy texture.

Substitution:
* *Substitute 1 cup chopped celery for the fennel.*

Vegetarian Substitution:
* *Substitute yogurt with soy or rice milk. One cup low-fat soy or rice sour cream can be used.*

Spring Vegetable Soup

SERVES 8

CALORIES PER SERVING: 92.1

FAT (G) PER SERVING: 0.8

The spring is a time when I love to visit the produce section of the supermarket, because of the abundance of fresh vegetables from all over North America. This soup is also an excellent way to use up vegetables you have sitting in your refrigerator.

6 cups vegetable stock (low-sodium/low-fat)
2 medium potatoes, cubed
1 small onion, chopped
2 cloves garlic, chopped
2 celery stalks, chopped
1 small zucchini, cubed
1/2 red OR green pepper, chopped
1 cup drained low-sodium frozen OR canned peas

1/2 cup frozen corn
1 19-oz can low-sodium crushed tomatoes
1 cup chopped button mushrooms
1/2 tsp black pepper
1/2 tsp dried basil
1/2 tsp dried thyme
1/2 tsp chili powder
1 bay leaf
1/2 cup chopped fresh parsley

In a large soup pot, heat 1 cup of the stock and gently sauté the potatoes for 4 to 5 minutes. Add the onion, garlic, celery, zucchini, red or green pepper, remaining stock, peas, corn, tomatoes, mushrooms, black pepper, basil, thyme, chili powder and bay leaf. Bring to a boil and reduce to a simmer for about 15 minutes. Remove the bay leaf. Garnish with parsley and serve piping hot with a salad.

Be sure to stretch—for at least 5 mintues—before and after every workout.

Substitutions:
• Replace the vegetables with any others you have or like.
• Replace the low-sodium vegetable stock with low-sodium chicken stock.

Grilled Vegetable Soup

SERVES 6

CALORIES PER SERVING: 805

FAT (G) PER SERVING: 1.1

The Grilled Vegetable Soup has a distinctive flavour that will have your guests and family asking, "How did you do this?"

1 small zucchini, sliced lengthwise
2 large carrots, sliced lengthwise
8 asparagus stalks
1 medium red onion, cut into thick circles
1 large red pepper, cut into wide strips
1 large green pepper, cut into wide strips
1 large Portobello mushroom
6 cups vegetable stock (low-sodium/low-fat)

1 14-oz can stewed tomatoes
1/4 cup chopped fresh basil
   OR 1/2 tsp dried
1 1/2 tbsp chopped fresh oregano
   OR 1/4 tsp dried
2 tbsp balsamic vinegar (optional)
1/2 tsp black pepper
1 bay leaf
1/4 cup fresh parsley

Place the zucchini, carrots, asparagus, onion, peppers and mushroom on a cookie sheet. Spray both sides sparingly with cooking spray and grill on an indoor grill, or barbecue about 5 minutes or until grill marks appear and vegetables turn golden. Chop vegetables into bite-sized cubes. In a large soup pot, combine the stock, tomatoes, basil, oregano, balsamic vinegar (if using), pepper and bay leaf. Bring to a boil and toss in grilled vegetables. Reduce heat to simmer another 10 minutes. Remove the bay leaf. Garnish with fresh parsley and serve.

Tone and developed muscles help absorb shock. Women are more prone to injury because they have less muscle mass.

Substitutions:
- *Substitute any other grilled vegetables that are in season.*
- *Substitute red wine or apple juice for the balsamic vinegar.*

Lentil and Tomato Soup

SERVES 6

CALORIES PER SERVING: 152

FAT (G) PER SERVING: 2.8

Lentils are a legume used worldwide in soups, salads and casseroles. The lentil found in North America is slightly smaller then a pea bean and greenish brown in colour. You can purchase lentils dry or in a can.

2 cups lentils (see Tip)
1 28-oz can crushed tomatoes
2 large plum tomatoes, chopped
6 cups vegetable stock (low-sodium/low-fat)
1 small onion, chopped

2 cloves garlic, chopped
1/2 tsp dried basil
1/2 tsp dried oregano
1/2 tsp black pepper
1/2 cup chopped fresh parsley
1 bay leaf
1/4 cup grated Parmesan cheese

In a large soup pot, combine the lentils, tomatoes, stock, onion, garlic, basil, oregano, black pepper, 1/4 cup of the parsley and the bay leaf. Bring to a boil. Reduce heat and simmer for 25 minutes. Remove the bay leaf. Using a hand blender, purée soup until it has a creamy texture. Serve immediately, garnished with the remaining parsley and Parmesan.

TIP

If you use dried lentils, soak them overnight in a bowl of water.

Substitution:
• Substitute 4 medium potatoes for the fresh tomatoes.

Vegetarian Substitution:
• Replace the Parmesan with a rice Parmesan.

Zucchini and Herb Soup

SERVES 6

CALORIES PER SERVING: 84.8

FAT (G) PER SERVING: 0.8

Zucchini is one of the most underrated vegetables. You'll love it in this soup.

6 cups vegetable stock (low-sodium/low-fat)
1 medium onion, chopped
1 clove garlic, chopped
6 medium zucchini, cubed small
2 small potatoes, cubed
1/4 cup dry white wine

1/2 tsp dried basil
1/2 tsp dried oregano
1/2 tsp dried thyme
1 tbsp dried parsley
    OR 1/2 cup chopped fresh
1/2 tsp black pepper
1 bay leaf

In a large non-stick soup pot, heat 1/4 cup of the stock and sauté the onion and garlic until translucent, about 2 minutes. Add the zucchini, potatoes, remaining stock, wine, basil, oregano, thyme, parsley, pepper and bay leaf. Bring to a boil and reduce to simmer. Simmer 20 minutes or until zucchini and potatoes are cooked. If the soup is too thick add some more stock or 1 cup non-fat or skim milk. Remove the bay leaf. With a hand blender, purée the soup and serve immediately.

TIP

Add mushrooms or cauliflower to thicken soup even more.

Substitutions:
- *You can replace any of the dried herbs with 2 tbsp chopped fresh herbs.*
- *If you don't want to add wine, use white grape juice or apple juice.*

Italian Mushroom Soup

SERVES 6

CALORIES PER SERVING: 64.9

FAT (G) PER SERVING: 0.7

In this soup, for a creamy texture without the cream, I add 2 potatoes and purée. This technique can be applied to other soups and sauces.

6 cups vegetable stock (low-sodium/low-fat)	4 cups chopped assorted mushrooms
1/2 tsp black pepper	1 medium onion, chopped
1/2 tsp dried basil	2 medium potatoes, cubed
1/2 tsp crushed dried rosemary	2 celery stalks, chopped
1/4 tsp dried thyme	1 bay leaf
	1/4 cup chopped fresh parsley

In a large soup pot, add the stock, pepper, basil, rosemary and thyme. Bring to a boil. Add the mushrooms, onion, potatoes, celery and bay leaf. Reduce heat to medium, cover and simmer about 20 minutes. Remove the bay leaf. Using a hand blender, purée the soup to a creamy consistency. Garnish with fresh parsley and serve hot.

TIP

- If the soup reduces, just add some more stock.
- This recipe is good for leftover potatoes.

Substitution:
- *Use the more common button mushrooms.*

Mushroom Soup with Cauliflower

SERVES 6

CALORIES PER SERVING: 38.4

FAT (G) PER SERVING: 0.9

Mushroom soup can taste different every time you prepare it. The taste depends on what herbs, spices and other fresh vegetables you choose to combine.

4 cups button mushrooms, chopped
2 cups chopped cauliflower
1 medium onion, chopped
2 cloves garlic, finely chopped
8 cups vegetable stock (low-sodium/low-fat)

1/2 cup chopped fresh parsley
1 tbsp chopped fresh rosemary OR 1/2 tsp dried
1 tbsp chopped fresh oregano OR 1/2 tsp dried
1/2 tsp black pepper
1 bay leaf

In a large soup pot, combine the mushrooms, cauliflower, onion, garlic, stock, 1/4 cup of the parsley, rosemary, oregano, pepper and bay leaf. Bring to a boil and reduce to a simmer. Simmer the soup about 20 minutes. Remove the bay leaf. Using a hand blender, purée the soup until it has a smooth, creamy texture. Garnish with the remaining fresh parsley.

Substitution:
• Substitute a combination of mushrooms such as Portobello, shiitake or porcini (these will add more flavour) for the button mushrooms.

Mushroom Soup with Potato and Cheese

SERVES 8

CALORIES PER SERVING: 86.3

FAT (G) PER SERVING: 1.7

Soup, soup, soup and more soup. I guess I just never get sick of a nice hearty bowl of soup.

6 cups vegetable stock (low-sodium/low-fat)
1/2 tsp dried basil
1/2 tsp dried thyme
1/2 tsp chili powder
1/2 tsp black pepper
4 cups button mushrooms, chopped

2 medium potatoes, cubed
1 medium onion, chopped
2 cloves garlic, finely chopped
2 cups 1% or skim milk
1/2 cup shredded low-fat cheddar cheese

In a large soup pot, bring stock to a boil. Add the basil, thyme, chili powder and pepper. Cook for about 5 minutes. Add the mushrooms, potatoes, onion and garlic. Simmer for 20 minutes until the potatoes are completely cooked. Using a hand blender, purée the soup to a creamy texture. Add the milk and cheese and mix well over low heat another 5 minutes.

TIP

If soup reduces too much, add more stock.

Substitution:
- *Substitute different types of mushrooms, such as oyster and Portobello, for the button mushrooms.*

Vegetarian Substitutions:
- *Substitute the milk with soy or rice milk.*
- *Substitute the cheese with a low-fat rice or soy cheddar.*

Sweet Potato Soup with Cinnamon and Apple

SERVES 8

CALORIES PER SERVING: 131.8

FAT (G) PER SERVING: 0.7

The sweet potato, one of my favourite root vegetables, is not a member of the potato family. (The origin of this root vegetable is South America, but it is widely grown throughout North America.)

6 cups soup stock (low-sodium/low-fat)
1 cup apple juice
1 cup applesauce
3 medium sweet potatoes, peeled and cubed (about 4 cups)
2 potatoes, peeled and cubed (about 1 cup)

2 apples, peeled, cored and cubed
1 small onion, chopped
1 tbsp lemon juice
1/2 tsp dried basil
1/2 tsp dried oregano
1/2 tsp cinnamon
1/2 tsp black pepper
1 bay leaf

In a large soup pot, combine stock, apple juice and applesauce. Bring to a boil; reduce heat to medium and add sweet potatoes, potatoes, apples, onion, lemon juice, basil, oregano, cinnamon, pepper and the bay leaf. Boil 10 minutes. Reduce to a simmer and cook another 10 minutes. Remove the bay leaf. Using a hand blender, purée the soup to a smooth and creamy texture. Serve hot.

Try posture-improving floor exercise classes like Pilates.

Substitution:
• Substitute yam for sweet potato.

Corn and Potato Chowder

SERVES 8

CALORIES PER SERVING: 139.6

FAT (G) PER SERVING: 1.4

A chowder is a meal within a meal. You can add leftover vegetables and day-old mashed potatoes.

6 cups vegetable stock (low-sodium/low-fat)	1/2 tsp dried basil
2 cloves garlic, chopped	1/2 tsp dried thyme
4 medium potatoes, boiled	1/2 tsp black pepper
2 cups corn	1/2 tsp salt
1 red pepper, diced	2 cups 1% or skim milk
1 medium onion, diced	1/2 cup chopped fresh parsley

In a large soup pot, combine the stock, garlic and potatoes. Simmer for 15 minutes or until potatoes are cooked. Using a hand blender, purée the potatoes to a creamy texture. Add the corn, red pepper, onion, basil, thyme, black pepper and salt. Simmer on low for 10 minutes; add the milk. Cook another 5 minutes until the chowder has a nice milky texture. Sprinkle with parsley and serve.

Watch what you eat. Dramatically cutting calories sends your body into fuel-conservation mode—your metabolism slows, making it even harder to lose weight.

Vegetarian Substitution:
• Substitute milk with soy or rice milk.

Mediterranean Fish Chowder

SERVES 8

CALORIES PER SERVING: 125.3

FAT (G) PER SERVING: 2.0

Soup can be a main meal in my house, and this Mediterranean fish chowder fits the bill.

6 cups fish OR vegetable stock
(low-sodium/low-fat)
1 medium red onion, chopped
2 cloves garlic, minced
2 celery stalks, chopped
2 carrots, chopped
1 red pepper, chopped
1 19-oz can stewed tomatoes,
chopped

1/2 tsp dried basil
1/2 tsp dried thyme
1/2 tsp dried sage
1/2 tsp black pepper
1 cup drained canned clams
1 small swordfish steak, cubed
(about 1 cup)
1 cup medium shrimp, peeled and
deveined

In a deep soup pot, heat 2 tbsp of the stock and sauté the onion and garlic for 3 minutes, being careful not to burn the garlic. Add the celery, carrots and red pepper; gently sauté another 3 minutes. Add tomatoes, remaining stock, basil, thyme, sage and pepper. Bring to a boil, reduce heat and simmer 15 minutes, stirring occasionally. Stir in clams, swordfish and shrimp. Simmer until seafood is cooked, about 5 to 7 minutes.

Substitution:
• Replace shrimp with squid, mussels or scallops.

Vegetarian Substitution:
• Substitute seafood with assortment of mushrooms such as button, Portobello and shiitake.

Dear Ken,

I work with a woman who watches Kenny and Mary Jo all the time, so much so that the rest of us in the department became very curious and began watching you, too. Now we watch you all the time and discuss the episodes on our coffee breaks. As far as we're concerned, Kenny and Mary Jo are the dynamic duo of cooking and inspire us all to "dabble" in culinary delights!

Thanks for being such a delight to watch.

The T.I.C. gang! (received by e-mail)

SALADS

Crouton Salad

SERVES 4

SALAD:

CALORIES PER SERVING: 107.3

FAT (G) PER SERVING: 1.3

DRESSING:

CALORIES PER SERVING: 13.5

FAT (G) PER SERVING: 0.1

This crouton bread salad is a perfect way to use up stale bread.

1 small red onion, cut into thin rings
2 celery stalks, chopped
1 red pepper, chopped
1 small cucumber, diced
1 cup chopped fresh parsley
1/4 cup chopped fresh dill
1/4 cup chopped fresh basil
2 cups home-made or purchased croutons

DRESSING:
1/4 cup apple juice
1 tbsp balsamic vinegar
1 tbsp white wine vinegar
1 tbsp lemon juice
1 clove garlic, minced
1/2 tsp black pepper
1/2 tsp chili powder

In a medium salad bowl, combine the onion, celery, red pepper, cucumber, parsley, dill and basil; toss. To prepare the dressing, in a blender or with a hand blender, blend the apple juice, balsamic vinegar, wine vinegar, lemon juice, garlic, pepper and chili powder. Add croutons to the salad and toss with the dressing. Refrigerate the salad for at least 30 minutes to allow the dressing to soak through the croutons.

Substitutions:
- *Use croutons made from stale French or Italian bread.*
- *Substitute a low-sodium/ low-fat vegetable stock for the apple juice.*

Asparagus with Mustard and Garlic Dressing

SERVES 4

CALORIES PER SERVING: 58.6

FAT (G) PER SERVING: 0.9

This asparagus salad is something I serve occasionally before the main course.

1 cup vegetable stock (low-sodium/low-fat)	1 tbsp non-fat sour cream
24 asparagus stalks	1 tbsp white wine vinegar
2 hearts romaine lettuce	1 tsp lemon juice
1 small red onion, sliced into thin rings	1/2 tsp black pepper
2 tbsp Dijon mustard	1/4 tsp dried basil
2 cloves garlic, finely chopped (optional)	1/4 tsp dried thyme
	1/4 tsp dried oregano

In a large sauté pan, bring the vegetable stock to a boil. Blanch the asparagus for 2 minutes. The asparagus will be bright green. Rinse in ice-cold water and drain well. Place the lettuce on a serving platter and arrange the asparagus and onion rings on top. To prepare the dressing, whisk together the mustard, garlic (if using), sour cream, vinegar, lemon juice, pepper, basil, thyme and oregano. Mix well and drizzle evenly over the salad.

Be sure to strengthen your abdominal muscles to help protect your lower-back muscles.

Substitution:
- *Substitute non-fat sour cream with non-fat yogurt.*

Vegetarian Substitution:
- *Substitute sour cream with low-fat soy or rice sour cream.*

Cucumber and Fennel Salad

SERVES 4

CALORIES PER SERVING: 170.2

FAT (G) PER SERVING: 14

Fresh cucumber and fennel make an excellent tangy salad, especially when combined with lemon and mint.

2 tbsp lemon juice	1 medium cucumber, chopped
1/4 cup canola oil	1 medium fennel bulb, chopped
1 tsp sugar	1 green pepper, chopped
1/2 tsp black pepper	1/2 cup chopped fresh parsley
1 tsp white wine vinegar	1/4 cup chopped fresh mint

In a medium salad bowl, combine the lemon juice, oil, sugar, black pepper and wine vinegar. Mix well. Add the cucumber, fennel, green pepper, parsley and mint. Toss.

Help to strengthen your bones by doing weight-bearing aerobic exercise such as running, brisk walking or stair climbing.

Substitution:
• *Substitute 1 medium zucchini, chopped, for the fennel.*

Pasta Salad with Cucumber and Feta

SERVES 6

CALORIES PER SERVING: 179.7

FAT (G) PER SERVING: 8.0

I often prepare a pasta salad as a side dish. In this salad, the feta cheese adds zing.

2 cups cooked fusilli	1 tsp dried oregano
1 medium cucumber, cubed	OR 2 tbsp chopped fresh
1 medium red pepper, chopped	1/2 tsp dried basil
1 medium green pepper, chopped	OR 1 tbsp chopped fresh
1 cup cooked green beans, chopped	2 tbsp canola oil
2 medium tomatoes, chopped	2 tbsp red wine vinegar
1/2 cup crumbled feta cheese	1 tsp balsamic vinegar
	1/2 tsp black pepper

In a medium mixing bowl, combine the pasta, cucumber, red pepper, green pepper, green beans, tomatoes and feta; sprinkle with oregano and basil. Mix salad well. In a small mixing bowl combine the oil, wine vinegar, balsamic vinegar and black pepper. Drizzle over the salad and serve.

Your metabolism starts to slow down in the late evening. Go easy on those late night snacks.

Substitution:
- *Replace feta with a light goat cheese.*

Vegetarian Substitution:
- *Substitute the feta with 1/2 cup chopped, pitted olives.*

Herbed Bean Salad with Lemon and Parsley

SERVES 6

CALORIES PER SERVING: 255.6

FAT (G) PER SERVING: 18.5

A bean salad is often served in Italy as a starter. This salad, made with lemon and parsley, is delicious, healthful, quick and easy.

1/2 cup canola oil	1 green pepper, chopped
3 tbsp lemon juice	1 bunch green onions, chopped
1 tsp white wine vinegar	1 cup finely chopped parsley
1/2 tsp black pepper	1/2 cup chopped basil
1/2 tsp Dijon mustard	OR 1/2 tsp dried
1 cup cooked red kidney beans	1 tbsp chopped thyme
1 cup cooked white lima beans	OR 1/4 tsp dried
1 red pepper, chopped	1 tsp lemon zest (optional)

In a medium mixing bowl, combine the oil, lemon juice, vinegar, black pepper and mustard. Mix well. Add the beans, red pepper, green pepper, green onions, parsley, basil and thyme. Mix well. Sprinkle with lemon zest (if using). Refrigerate 30 minutes before serving.

Substitutions:
- *Substitute other beans or peas.*
- *Substitute 1/2 cup chopped fresh coriander for parsley and replace the Dijon mustard with a mild curry paste.*

Grilled Chicken Salad with Pear and Blue Cheese

SERVES 4

CALORIES PER SERVING: 244.4

FAT (G) PER SERVING: 4.2

The Grilled Chicken Salad with Pear and Blue Cheese is one of my favourite light meals.

4 boned, skinless chicken breasts	2 tbsp non-fat yogurt
1/2 cup pear nectar	1/2 tsp black pepper
2 pears, quartered and cored	2 heads romaine lettuce
1/2 cup chopped fresh mint	1 small red onion, thinly sliced
2 tbsp crumbled blue cheese	1/2 cup grated carrot
1 tsp white wine vinegar	8 cherry tomatoes
1/2 tsp balsamic vinegar	

Brush both sides of chicken with 1/4 cup of the pear nectar. Grill for 15 minutes or until chicken is cooked through and has grill marks. Allow to cool and slice. Grill the pears for 5 minutes. Combine remaining pear nectar, mint, blue cheese, wine vinegar, balsamic vinegar, yogurt and pepper. Mix well. On 4 plates, arrange lettuce, red onion and carrots. Put the chicken breast on top of each salad and drizzle with the dressing. Garnish with 2 cherry tomatoes on the side of each salad.

A well-rounded exercise program includes aerobic exercise, strength training and stretching.

Substitution:
• *Substitute turkey for the chicken.*

Orange Turkey with Spinach

SERVES 4

CALORIES PER SERVING: 247.5

FAT (G) PER SERVING: 7.9

The orange flavour in this turkey salad adds tang and zest to ordinary ingredients that you probably have at home.

1 cup orange juice	1 tbsp rice wine vinegar
1 cup vegetable stock (low-sodium/low-fat)	1 clove garlic, chopped
1/4 cup chopped fresh mint OR 1/2 tsp dried	1/2 tsp black pepper
	4 cups shredded spinach
1 medium boned, skinless turkey breast, sliced into strips	1 red pepper, sliced
	1 large orange, peeled and cut into small wedges
2 tbsp canola oil	1 tbsp orange zest
1 tbsp orange juice concentrate	

In a sauté pan, combine the orange juice, stock and 1/2 cup of the mint. Bring to a boil; reduce to simmer and add the turkey strips. Poach turkey 15 minutes or until completely white and cooked through. Remove the turkey and allow to cool. In a small mixing bowl, combine the oil, orange juice concentrate, vinegar, garlic and black pepper. Place the spinach in a medium glass salad bowl. Add the turkey, red pepper and orange wedges. Drizzle with dressing and sprinkle on the orange zest for zest.

An exercise program is an excellent way to stay healthy. To ward off injury and to keep boredom at bay, aim for variety in your activities.

Substitution:
• Substitute chicken for turkey, or sliced grilled Portobello mushrooms for a vegetarian option.

Grilled Steak Salad with Creamy Garlic Mustard

SERVES 4

CALORIES PER SERVING: 194.3

FAT (G) PER SERVING: 5.7

This grilled steak salad makes a great light lunch or dinner. I also use the dressing as a marinade for chicken or beef.

1 tbsp black pepper	2 tbsp Dijon mustard
1 tsp onion powder	1 tbsp balsamic vinegar
1 tsp chili powder	1 tbsp lemon juice
1/2 tsp dried thyme	1 tsp Worcestershire sauce
2 26-oz New York steaks	1/2 tsp dried basil
3 cloves garlic, chopped	2 hearts romaine lettuce
1/2 cup low-fat OR	1 small red onion, thinly sliced
non-fat yogurt	10 cherry tomatoes

Combine 1 1/2 tsp of the pepper, the onion powder, chili powder and thyme. Mix well and sprinkle evenly on the steaks. Using an indoor or outdoor grill, place the steaks on high and sear both sides. Grill until desired doneness. Cool and slice thinly. In a blender, combine the garlic, yogurt, mustard balsamic vinegar, lemon juice, Worcestershire sauce, basil and remaining pepper. Blend until smooth. Arrange the romaine lettuce, onion and cherry tomatoes on a deep serving platter, place the steak on the salad and pour over the dressing.

Substitution:
• Substitute chicken breast for steaks.

Sesame Grilled Steak and Bean Salad

SERVES 6

CALORIES PER SERVING: 221.2

FAT (G) PER SERVING: 13.2

If you prefer vegetarian, replace the steak with sliced, grilled Porto-bello mushrooms.

3 tbsp sesame oil	1/2 lb fresh green beans, cut on diagonal
1 tsp canola oil	1/2 lb fresh yellow beans, cut on diagonal
2 tsp rice wine vinegar	
1 tsp lemon juice	2 hearts romaine lettuce
1/2 tsp mild curry powder or chili powder	1 cup cherry tomatoes, cut in half
1 tsp black pepper	1 tsp sesame seeds
1 lb round steak, 1-inch thick, trimmed of fat	

In a small mixing bowl, combine 2 tbsp of the sesame oil, the canola oil, vinegar, lemon juice, curry powder and 1/2 tsp of the pepper. Mix well and set aside. Gently brush both sides of the steak with the remaining sesame oil and sprinkle with the remaining pepper. Grill until grill marks appear or, for medium, 3 minutes each side, longer for well done. Remove and allow to cool. In a pot of boiling water, blanch the beans for 4 minutes; rinse in cold water and drain. Cut the steak into thin strips. On a large serving platter, arrange the lettuce and then place the steak and beans on top. Place cherry tomatoes around the salad. Drizzle the dressing over salad and sprinkle with sesame seeds.

Substitution:
• Substitute grilled chicken or turkey for the steak.

Seafood Salad with Lemon and Lemon Oil

SERVES 6

CALORIES PER SERVING: 359.6

FAT (G) PER SERVING: 19.9

I usually serve this as a main course at lunch.

2 cups dry white wine
2 cloves garlic, chopped
Juice of 1 lemon
2 tbsp chopped fresh dill
12 medium shrimp, peeled and deveined
16 medium scallops
1 10-oz can clams, drained
1 6-oz can crabmeat, drained

DRESSING:

1/2 cup canola oil
Juice of 2 lemons
2 tbsp white wine vinegar
1 tsp chopped fresh dill
1 clove garlic, chopped
1 tsp black pepper
1 tsp dried oregano

In a large frying pan or sauté pan, combine the wine, garlic, lemon juice and dill. Bring to a boil and reduce to a simmer. Add the shrimp, scallops and clams. Simmer 4 minutes or until the scallops turn white and the shrimp turn pink. Remove the seafood. Place in a large salad bowl and add the crabmeat. Chill for 1 hour or let cool.

To prepare the dressing, in a small mixing bowl, combine the oil, lemon juice, vinegar, dill, garlic, black pepper and oregano. Mix the dressing well and combine with the cooled seafood.

TIP

Chill the seafood salad with dressing at least 1 hour. It should be served chilled but not too cold.

Substitution:
• *Substitute swordfish cut into 1-inch cubes for the scallops.*

Shrimp and Fennel Salad

SERVES 4

CALORIES PER SERVING: 149.4

FAT (G) PER SERVING: 7.8

Shrimp makes a wonderful light salad any time of the year. The fennel adds a slightly minty flavour.

24 medium cooked shrimp (peeled)
1 medium fennel bulb, thinly sliced
1 small red pepper, thinly sliced
1 small red onion, thinly sliced
1/2 cup fresh parsley, chopped
1/4 cup chopped fresh mint or tarragon OR 1/2 tsp dried

2 heads Boston lettuce
3 tbsp white wine vinegar
2 tbsp canola oil
1/2 tsp dried basil
1/2 tsp dried oregano
1/2 tsp black pepper

In a medium mixing bowl combine the shrimp, fennel, red pepper, onion, parsley and mint. Mix well. Line a fancy glass salad bowl with the Boston lettuce. Add shrimp salad mixture. In a small mixing bowl, combine the vinegar, oil, basil, oregano and black pepper. Mix well, drizzle over the salad and serve.

Replenish your energy stores (food) within 2 hours of your workouts.

Substitution:
• *Substitute 3 cups medium cooked scallops for the shrimp.*

Vegetarian Substitution:
• *Substitute 1 cup chopped zucchini and 1 cup chopped mushrooms for shrimp.*

DRESSINGS

Low-Fat Caesar Dressing

SERVES 6

CALORIES PER SERVING: 26.1

FAT (G) PER SERVING: 0.4

The No-Mayo, No-Oil Caesar Dressing on the television show was a real crowd pleaser. I received so many letters and comments I've decided to do another version of this popular dressing.

4 cloves garlic	1 tbsp lemon juice
1/2 cup non-fat sour cream	1 tbsp balsamic vinegar
1 tsp anchovy paste OR 1 anchovy, mashed (optional)	1/2 tsp black pepper
	1/2 tsp chili powder (optional)
1 tbsp Worcestershire sauce	2 tbsp grated low-fat Parmesan
1 tbsp low-sodium soy sauce	cheese

In a blender, purée the garlic, sour cream, anchovy paste (if using), Worcestershire sauce, soy sauce, lemon juice, balsamic vinegar, pepper, chili powder (if using) and Parmesan until smooth. Serve with 2 heads of romaine lettuce using only the heart sections or 1 head of romaine using all of it.

To maintain your weight, you need to consume 15 calories for each pound that you weigh.

Substitution:
• Replace the non-fat sour cream with non-fat yogurt.

Another Caesar Dressing

MAKES 1 CUP

CALORIES PER TABLESPOON: 11.9

FAT (G) PER TABLESPOON: 0.3

I use this dressing on salads that include poultry, fish or meat.

4 cloves garlic	2 tbsp lemon juice
1 shallot	2 tbsp white wine vinegar
1/2 cup non-fat yogurt	1/2 tsp black pepper
2 tbsp grated low-fat Parmesan cheese	1/2 tsp Worcestershire sauce
2 tbsp non-fat sour cream	1/2 tsp anchovy paste (optional)

In a food processor, combine garlic, shallot, yogurt, Parmesan, sour cream, lemon juice, vinegar, pepper, Worcestershire sauce and anchovy paste (if using). Purée. This dressing will last, covered in the refrigerator, for about a week.

If you are a beginner to strength training, lighten the load and slow it down. Lighter work outs with lighter weights may keep you on course.

Garlic-Lemon Salad Dressing

MAKES ABOUT 1 CUP

CALORIES PER TABLESPOON: 62.1

FAT (G) PER TABLESPOON: 6.8

I always have this dressing on hand in the refrigerator.

1/2 cup canola oil	1 tsp white wine vinegar
3 tbsp lemon juice	1/2 tsp black pepper
2 cloves garlic	1/2 tsp dried tarragon
1 tbsp lemon zest	1/4 tsp sea salt
1 tsp balsamic vinegar	

In a blender or using a hand blender, combine oil, lemon juice, garlic, zest, balsamic vinegar, wine vinegar, pepper, tarragon and salt. Purée. Keep refrigerated; shake before using. This dressing will last 1 week.

Don't participate in competitive events, such as 5 kilometre runs, during the hottest part of the day. Try to complete your runs early in the day if possible or in the late afternoon.

Garlic-Dill Dressing

MAKES 2 CUPS

CALORIES PER TABLESPOON: 3.3

FAT (G) PER TABLESPOON: 0.0

This is a perfect dressing with romaine lettuce. I occasionally dilute it with 1 more cup of vegetable stock and use it as a marinade for fish, poultry, meat or vegetables.

3 cloves garlic	2 tbsp lemon juice
1/2 cup non-fat yogurt	1 tbsp chopped fresh parsley
1/2 cup vegetable stock (low-sodium/low-fat)	1 tbsp balsamic vinegar
1/4 cup dill, chopped	1/2 tsp black pepper

In a blender or using a hand blender, combine garlic, yogurt, stock, dill, lemon juice, parsley, vinegar and pepper. Purée.

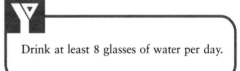

Drink at least 8 glasses of water per day.

Honey and Mustard Sauce

MAKES 1 CUP

CALORIES PER TABLESPOON: 20.7

FAT (G) PER TABLESPOON: 0.2

This Honey and Mustard Sauce is great with poultry, meat or seafood.

2 tbsp vegetable stock (low-sodium/low-fat)	3 tbsp Dijon mustard
2 cloves garlic, finely chopped	1 tsp balsamic vinegar
1/2 cup non-fat sour cream	1/2 tsp dried basil
1/2 cup non-fat yogurt	1/2 tsp black pepper
	2 tbsp liquid honey

In a saucepan, heat the stock and sauté the garlic about 2 minutes. Add the sour cream and cook, stirring, for another 2 minutes. Do not boil. Add the yogurt, mustard, balsamic vinegar, basil and pepper. Continue to stir about 5 minutes or until the liquid has reduced to a fourth. Stir in the honey and serve warm.

You are never too old to exercise. Your muscles respond positively to exercise even when you are approaching 100 years of age.

Pesto Sauce with No Oil

SERVES 4 TO 6

CALORIES PER SERVING: 15.0

FAT (G) PER SERVING: 0.4

One of my favourite sauces for pasta is pesto. Here is a similar-tasting sauce without the fat or as many calories.

2 cups fresh basil
4 cloves garlic
1 cup chopped mushrooms
1 cup vegetable stock (low-sodium/low-fat)

2 tbsp grated low-fat Parmesan cheese
1/2 tsp black pepper

In a blender or food processor, combine the basil, garlic, mushrooms, stock, Parmesan cheese and pepper. Blend until smooth. Transfer to a large sauté pan and simmer until reduced by half, about 5 minutes. Add cooked pasta, mix well and cook another minute. Serve immediately.

Sweet Red Pepper Sauce

SERVES 6

CALORIES PER SERVING: 50.8

FAT (G) PER SERVING: 0.3

This Sweet Red Pepper Sauce adds flavour to pasta, rice and even chicken or fish (as a relish on top). I do a few versions of this, so experiment on your own with other ingredients.

4 medium red peppers, chopped
1 medium red onion, chopped
1 cup vegetable stock (low-sodium/low-fat)

1/2 cup apple juice
1/4 cup fresh mint
1/2 tsp black pepper

In a food processor, combine red peppers, onion, stock, apple juice, mint and black pepper; purée until smooth. Serve cold over fish, meat or poultry. Or simmer for 10 minutes and serve hot. If liquid reduces too much, add more stock or, for a sweeter taste, more apple juice.

Muscle will not turn to fat when you stop lifting weights. The muscle only reduces in size.

Substitution:
• Replace apple juice with grape juice. Replace fresh mint with basil.

Tomato Sauce with Herbs

SERVES 6

CALORIES PER SERVING: 78.0

FAT (G) PER SERVING: 0.5

I use this sauce with pasta, rice, pizza, poultry and fish. Occasionally, I add it to soups and stews.

1 28-oz can stewed tomatoes	1/2 cup diced carrots
2 cloves garlic, chopped	1/2 cup apple juice
1 small onion, diced	1 tsp chili powder
2 celery stalks, chopped	1/2 tsp dried basil
1 small green pepper, diced	1/2 tsp dried oregano
1 cup low-sodium tomato juice	1/2 tsp dried rosemary
1/2 cup finely chopped mushrooms	1 bay leaf

In a large saucepan, combine the tomatoes, garlic, onion, celery, green pepper, tomato juice, mushrooms, carrots, apple juice, chili powder, basil, oregano, rosemary and the bay leaf. Bring to a boil and reduce heat to simmer for 20 minutes or until liquid has reduced by half. Remove the bay leaf. Serve with cooked pasta.

Substitution:
• Substitute or add any other vegetables. But keep in the finely chopped mushrooms—they add to the smooth texture of the sauce.

Warm Apple and Ginger Sauce

MAKES 1 CUP

CALORIES PER TABLESPOON: 21.0

FAT (G) PER TABLESPOON: 0.1

This easy-to-prepare sauce is great with pork or beef.

2 apples, peeled, cored and chopped	1/2 cup non-fat sour cream
1/2 cup apple juice	1 tsp low-sodium soy sauce
1/2 cup non-fat yogurt	1/2 tsp dried oregano
1 tsp grated fresh ginger	1/2 tsp black pepper

In a saucepan, combine the apples and apple juice; simmer for 10 minutes or until the apple has softened. With a hand blender, purée until smooth. Add the yogurt and ginger. Stir until smooth, about 2 minutes. Add the sour cream and continue to stir another 2 minutes. Add soy sauce, oregano and black pepper. Cook, stirring, on low heat 4 minutes or until smooth. Serve warm.

Cover your head when exercising outdoors in the cold. Heat loss from the head and neck may account for as much as 50% of your total heat loss.

Strawberry and Lemon
Salad Dressing

SERVES 6

CALORIES PER SERVING: 50.1

FAT (G) PER SERVING: 2.4

This salad dressing can also be used to baste fish, meat, poultry or vegetables when grilling or roasting. I occasionally use a salad dressing as a marinade before grilling.

3/4 cup fresh strawberries	2 tbsp white wine vinegar
1/2 cup non-fat yogurt	2 tbsp lemon juice
1/2 cup apple juice	1 tbsp lemon zest
1/2 cup chopped fresh parsley	1 tbsp canola oil
1/4 cup chopped fresh mint	

In a blender or with a hand blender, purée the strawberries, yogurt, apple juice, parsley, mint, vinegar, lemon juice, lemon zest and oil.

Substitution:
• Replace strawberries with ripe pear and apple juice with white grape or pear juice.

Dear Ken,

I just love your show! I discovered it a couple of months ago while surfing the channels, eating an uninspired supper in front of the TV. You make it seem easy and—most importantly—fun. Cooking has never really interested me but now I can't wait for the show to come on. I even tape it if I think I'll be late getting home from work.

I'm not sure which I enjoy more, when you "steal" the viewer mail or when Mary Jo picks on you ... You both seem like nice people, a lot of fun and a little wild at times, which is all the better. Keep up the good, no GREAT, work!

Sharon in Saint John, New Brunswick

SIDE DISHES

Baked Broccoli with Lemon and Cheese

SERVES 6

CALORIES PER SERVING: 54.4

FAT (G) PER SERVING: 1.1

Who hates broccoli? Try this citrus version and I guarantee you will love it.

3 cups broccoli florets	1/2 cup low-fat, shredded
1/2 cup lemon juice	cheddar cheese
1/2 tsp dried tarragon OR parsley	1 tbsp lemon zest

Place the broccoli in a baking dish and pour lemon juice over top. Sprinkle with the tarragon and cheddar cheese. Sprinkle the lemon zest over the cheese and bake in a preheated oven at 350°F for 15 minutes or until cheese is bubbling. Serve warm.

> Numerous studies have shown that people who exercise regularly have better memories, better reaction times, and better levels of concentration than people who don't exercise.

Baked Fennel and Peppers

SERVES 8

CALORIES PER SERVING: 54.8

FAT (G) PER SERVING: 0.6

I often use fennel to flavour soups, salads, stews and main courses. Serve this easy-to-prepare side dish with fish, chicken or beef. I have even made it a main dish in a vegetarian meal by adding more fennel and other vegetables.

2 fennel bulbs, cut into 1-inch pieces	4 celery stalks, cut into 1-inch pieces
2 red peppers, diced	1/2 tsp garlic powder
2 green peppers, diced	1/2 tsp dried oregano
1 medium red onion, cut into wedges	1/2 tsp dried rosemary
	1/2 tsp black pepper

In a non-stick baking dish, combine the fennel, red peppers, green peppers, onion and celery. Spray with a low-fat cooking spray for about 4 seconds. Sprinkle with the garlic powder, oregano, rosemary and black pepper; mix well. (If you want, you can combine the seasonings in a small bowl and then sprinkle.) Bake in a preheated oven at 350°F for about 35 minutes, turning once, until tender.

Exercise is one of the few activities that are effective in raising your level of HDL—the "good" cholesterol that lowers your risk of heart disease.

Substitution:
• Substitute potatoes, yams or even turnip for the peppers. You will have to cook harder vegetables about 15 minutes more.

Balsamic Grilled Eggplant

SERVES 6

CALORIES PER SERVING: 28.8

FAT (G) PER SERVING: 0.2

I especially like to serve eggplant grilled, which enhances its flavour and takes very little time to prepare. I like to use an indoor grill.

1 medium eggplant, sliced into circles	1/2 tsp garlic powder
2 tsp balsamic vinegar	1/2 tsp dried oregano
1/2 tsp dried basil	1/2 tsp black pepper

Brush both sides of the eggplant with the balsamic vinegar. In a small bowl combine the basil, garlic powder, oregano and pepper; sprinkle over both sides of the eggplant. Grill eggplant 4 minutes on each side or until grill marks appear.

Take at least 1 day off per week from physical activity.

Carrots with Basil and Tomato

SERVES 4

CALORIES PER SERVING: 92

FAT (G) PER SERVING: 0.4

I like to take everyday vegetables and combine them with each other to make different and enticing side dishes.

1 19-oz can diced stewed tomatoes	2 cups sliced carrot
	1/2 tsp black pepper
1/2 cup chopped fresh basil	1/4 cup dry red wine OR water

In a sauté pan, heat the tomatoes. Add the basil and cook for about 2 minutes. Add the carrots, pepper and wine. Simmer 10 minutes or until carrots are tender.

> Be sure to cross-train (do different exercises) so that you don't overwork your muscles.

Chili Ratatouille

SERVES 8

CALORIES PER SERVING: 77.6

FAT (G) PER SERVING: 0.9

The Chili Ratatouille as a side dish offers up a fine selection of vegetables you may have on hand or can get easily at your local supermarket. This ratatouille has such a variety of vegetables and herbs that it could be served as a vegetarian meal for four.

1 medium zucchini, chopped or diced	2 tomatoes, chopped
1 medium onion, chopped	2 tbsp chili powder
1 medium eggplant, diced	1/2 tsp cayenne (optional)
2 red peppers, chopped	1/2 tsp black pepper
1 green pepper, chopped	1/2 cup chopped fresh parsley
1 small yellow squash, chopped into squares	1/2 cup chopped fresh basil
	2 tbsp chopped fresh rosemary
4 cloves garlic, chopped	3 tbsp balsamic vinegar
	1 tbsp lemon juice

In a large non-stick baking dish, combine the zucchini, onion, eggplant, red peppers, green pepper, squash, garlic, tomatoes, chili powder, cayenne (if using), black pepper, 1/4 cup of the parsley, 1/4 cup of the basil and 1 tbsp of the rosemary. Mix well and bake in a preheated oven at 350°F for 25 minutes or until vegetables are tender but not too soft. In a small mixing bowl, combine the remaining parsley, basil and rosemary, the balsamic vinegar and lemon juice. Mix in with the vegetables and serve warm or at room temperature.

Try out long, earthy excursion-type exercises such as hiking, running, golf and trail walking.

Tangy Fruit Ratatouille

SERVES 4

CALORIES PER SERVING: 162.3

FAT (G) PER SERVING: 0.9

Every time I serve this dish my guests comment on having this fruit mixture as a vegetable. I occasionally serve this fruit ratatouille on top of fish or poultry. Experiment on your own and let me know.

1 Granny Smith apple, cored and chopped
1 Bartlett pear, cored and chopped
1 cup strawberries
2 peaches, chopped
2 nectarines, chopped
1 navel orange, peeled and chopped
1/2 cup fresh mint, chopped

1/2 cup fresh parsley, chopped
1/2 cup applesauce
1/2 cup cranberry OR orange juice
1 tsp chopped fresh ginger (optional)
1 tsp rice wine vinegar
1/4 tsp cinnamon
1 tbsp orange zest

In a large saucepan, combine all of the fruit, the mint, parsley, applesauce, juice, ginger (if using), vinegar and cinnamon. Heat gently for 8 or 10 minutes or until liquid has reduced by half. Serve warm sprinkled with orange zest.

TIP

This dish is best served with fish or poultry.

Substitution:
• *Substitute any other fruit.*

Vegetable-Stuffed Zucchini

SERVES 6

CALORIES PER SERVING: 51.5

FAT (G) PER SERVING: 0.4

The wonderful thing about this dish is that it can be served hot or cold. I sometimes use it instead of a small salad.

3 large zucchini	1 small carrot, shredded
1/2 cup tomato juice	1 celery stalk, chopped
1 small onion, chopped	1/2 cup chopped fennel
2 cloves garlic, chopped	1/4 cup mint, chopped
1 cup button mushrooms,	OR 1/2 tsp dried
chopped	1/2 tsp black pepper
1/2 cup chopped red pepper	1 tbsp lemon juice

Cut ends off the zucchini and cut into 3-inch pieces. Scoop out most of the centre, leaving about 1/2-inch in bottom. In a sauté pan over medium heat, heat the tomato juice. Sauté the onion and garlic for about 2 minutes. Add the mushrooms, red pepper, carrot, celery, fennel, mint, black pepper and lemon juice. Cook, stirring, about 4 minutes. Stuff each zucchini piece with the mixture and arrange in a baking pan. Bake in a preheated oven at 350°F for about 15 minutes. Serve hot or at room temperature.

Find a workout partner for encouragement and motivation.

Substitution:
• Substitute apple or grape juice for the tomato juice.

Corn Medley

SERVES 6

CALORIES PER SERVING: 38.3

FAT (G) PER SERVING: 0.7

Corn adds nutrition and colour to your plate.

1/2 cup vegetable stock (low-sodium/low-fat)	1 cup button mushrooms, chopped
1 cup frozen corn	1/2 tsp chili powder
1 small red pepper, chopped	1/2 tsp dried mint
	1 tsp calorie-reduced margarine

In a saucepan, heat the stock and add the corn, red pepper, mushrooms, chili powder and mint. Simmer on high for 5 minutes or until the stock has reduced by half. Stir in the margarine and serve immediately.

Do you need an adrenaline rush? Try something different, like river rafting for a "natural high."

Green Beans with Onion and Garlic

SERVES 4

CALORIES PER SERVING: 45.2

FAT (G) PER SERVING: 0.3

Green beans, usually available year round, make a perfect side dish.

3/4 cup vegetable stock (low-
    sodium/low-fat)
1 clove garlic, chopped
1 small onion, chopped

1 lb green beans
1/2 tsp dried basil
1/2 tsp black pepper

In a medium sauté pan, heat the vegetable stock and sauté the garlic and onion for about 2 minutes. Add the beans, basil and black pepper. Sauté the beans for 8 minutes or until tender but not overcooked.

Researchers have found that moderately depressed individuals who engage in aerobic exercise for 15 to 30 minutes at least every other day typically experience a positive mood swing within 2 to 3 weeks.

Herbed Roasted Onions and Mushrooms

SERVES 6

CALORIES PER SERVING: 51.6

FAT (G) PER SERVING: 0.6

When I prepare a dinner I always try to make simple but different side dishes—side dishes that are interesting and healthful but do not take 2 days to prepare.

1/2 tsp dried basil
1/2 tsp dried oregano
1/2 tsp dried rosemary
1/2 tsp dried thyme

1/2 tsp garlic powder
1/2 tsp black pepper
4 large red onions, cut into wedges
2 cups small button mushrooms

In a small mixing bowl, combine basil, oregano, rosemary, thyme, garlic powder and pepper. Place the onions and mushrooms on a non-stick cookie sheet or in a non-stick baking dish. Spray the vegetables with cooking spray for about 4 seconds. Sprinkle with the herb mixture and bake uncovered in a preheated oven at 350°F for 25 minutes or until tender.

Try tai chi for a Zen-like approach to fitness.

Substitution:
• Substitute other dried spices and herbs such as chili powder, curry powder or paprika.

Roasted Portobello Mushrooms with Onion and Garlic

SERVES 4

CALORIES PER SERVING: 37

FAT (G) PER SERVING: 0.1

The main course for a dinner takes long enough, so the side dishes should be easy and quick as well as flavourful and healthful. If you are a mushroom lover, you will want to try this side dish.

4 large Portobello mushrooms, sliced (about 6 cups)	2 cloves garlic, chopped
1 medium red onion, sliced	1/2 tsp dried thyme
1 small red pepper, sliced	1/4 cup vegetable stock (low-sodium/low-fat) OR apple juice

Place the mushrooms, onion, red pepper, garlic and thyme in a deep, non-stick baking dish and mix well. (If you would like to add other dried herbs, such as oregano, basil or rosemary, you can at this time.) Add the stock and bake in a preheated oven at 350°F for 20 minutes, mixing once. Do not overcook.

Substitution:
• Substitute small whole button mushrooms for Portobello mushrooms.

Roasted Asparagus with Lemon and Mint

SERVES 4

CALORIES PER SERVING: 16.7

FAT (G) PER SERVING: 0.2

The combination of asparagus and lemon in a side dish gives you the nutrition you require in your daily diet but also a twist for an old favourite.

12 medium asparagus stalks	1/2 tsp dried mint
Juice of 1 lemon	1/4 tsp black pepper
1 tbsp lemon zest	

Trim off the rough ends of the asparagus and place stalks on sheet of foil wrap. Cover the asparagus completely with the lemon juice. Sprinkle on the lemon zest, mint and pepper. Seal the foil, leaving space inside for steam. Bake in a preheated oven at 350°F for 10 minutes or until tender. Do not overcook.

Improve your co-ordination and agility by trying new exercise programs such as "box-fit" or skipping.

Spicy Grilled Vegetables

SERVES 6

CALORIES PER SERVING: 50.4

FAT (G) PER SERVING: 0.9

A grilled vegetable platter is a favourite as a side dish, appetizer or even salad with an additional dressing.

1/2 tsp dried basil	1 medium eggplant, sliced
1/2 tsp dried oregano	2 medium zucchini, sliced lengthwise
1/2 tsp dried rosemary	1 red onion, cut into wedges
1/2 tsp paprika	4 medium Portobello mushrooms
1/2 tsp cayenne	12 asparagus stalks
1/2 tsp garlic powder (optional)	1/4 cup balsamic vinegar

In a small bowl, combine the basil, oregano, rosemary, paprika, cayenne and garlic powder (if using). Place eggplant, zucchini, onion, mushrooms and asparagus on a platter and spray with cooking spray about 5 seconds. Add herb mixture and grill for about 2 minutes, and then sprinkle with the herb mixture, turning vegetables once to get grill marks. Grill for 2 to 3 minutes more. Place on the serving platter and drizzle with the balsamic vinegar. Serve warm or at room temperature.

Substitution:
- *Substitute other vegetables such as corn, peppers or cauliflower.*

Sautéed Spinach with Peppers

SERVES 6

CALORIES PER SERVING: 43.8

FAT (G) PER SERVING: 0.4

When I was growing up, spinach was not my favourite vegetable. A lot has changed since then! Try this flavourful version.

1 cup vegetable stock (low-sodium/low-fat)	1 green pepper, sliced
1 medium red onion, sliced	1 red pepper, sliced
1 clove garlic, chopped	1 tsp balsamic vinegar
1 lb fresh spinach, chopped	1/2 tsp black pepper

In a wok or deep sauté pan, bring the vegetable stock to a boil. Add the onion and garlic. Cook about 2 minutes. Then add the spinach by handfuls. The spinach will wilt; keep stirring. Add the peppers and cook about 8 minutes or until liquid has reduced. Remove to a bowl or plate and sprinkle with the balsamic vinegar and black pepper.

You lose weight and body fat when you expend more calories than you consume, not because you burn fat (or anything else) when you exercise.

Stuffed Red Peppers with Rice and Spinach

SERVES 4

CALORIES PER SERVING: 219.6

FAT (G) PER SERVING: 1.0

This is a great recipe for leftover rice.

4 medium red peppers
2 cups cooked rice
1 small red onion, chopped
2 cups shredded spinach
1/2 cup frozen corn
1 tbsp white wine vinegar

1 tsp chili powder
1/2 tsp dried basil
1/2 tsp black pepper
1/4 cup grated low-fat Parmesan cheese

Core the peppers and, if necessary, cut a thin slice from bottoms so they stand upright. In a medium mixing bowl, combine rice, onion, spinach, corn, vinegar, chili powder, basil and black pepper. Mix well and fill the peppers with the rice mixture. Place peppers in a baking dish just large enough to hold them. Sprinkle with the Parmesan cheese and bake in a preheated oven at 350°F for 15 minutes.

Don't forget to stretch after your workout.

Substitution:
• Substitute couscous for the rice.

Rice with Apples and Raisins

SERVES 4

CALORIES PER SERVING: 293.6

FAT (G) PER SERVING: 0.7

I sometimes cook rice in orange juice and add orange zest and mint, or chopped banana and raisins, towards the end of the cooking time.

2 1/2 cups apple juice   1/4 cup raisins
1 cup white rice   1/4 tsp cinnamon
1 apple, cored and chopped

In a medium saucepan, bring the apple juice to a boil and add the rice, apple, raisins and cinnamon. Reduce to a simmer and cook, covered for 15 minutes. If the liquid reduces too fast stir in more apple juice. Serve immediately.

Exercise should not be painful. A feeling of discomfort is generally a sign that you're asking your body to do something that it is not used to doing.

Sautéed Apple, Pear and Nectarine in Mint

SERVES 4

CALORIES PER SERVING: 143.2

FAT (G) PER SERVING: 0.8

The Sautéed Apple, Pear and Nectarine in Mint makes a wonderful variation on a vegetable side dish. I often serve this on top of fish or grilled chicken.

1 cup unsweetened apple juice

1 small red onion, sliced

1/2 tsp dried mint OR

1/4 cup chopped fresh mint

2 apples, cored and cubed

1 Bartlett pear, cored and cubed

2 nectarines, cubed

In a sauté pan, bring the apple juice to a boil. Reduce to medium heat and gently sauté the onion for about 3 minutes or until translucent. Stir in the mint, apples, pear and nectarine; sauté on medium heat about 10 minutes. Serve hot, warm or at room temperature.

Substitutions:
- *Replace the fruit with other firm fruit. Peaches can be used, but don't cook them too long. Add separately and sauté about 3 minutes only.*
- *Replace apple juice with pear juice or cranberry juice.*

Low-Fat Scalloped Potatoes

SERVES 4

CALORIES PER SERVING: 182.4

FAT (G) PER SERVING: 1.6

My neighbour Gill makes the best scalloped potatoes. This is my low-fat version that even she has had to compliment.

4 medium potatoes, thinly sliced	1/2 tsp black pepper
1 medium onion, thinly sliced	1/4 cup shredded low-fat
1 cup non-fat sour cream	cheddar cheese
1/2 tsp dried basil	1/4 cup grated low-fat Parmesan
1/2 tsp garlic powder	cheese

In a mixing bowl, combine the potatoes, onion, sour cream, basil, garlic powder and pepper. Lay out in a non-stick baking dish and sprinkle with the cheddar and Parmesan cheese. Bake in a preheated oven at 350°F for 20 minutes or until the potatoes are cooked through and the topping starts to turn golden.

Join a group of people who love to walk. Or better yet, organize a group in your neighbourhood.

Roasted Potatoes with Garlic and Chives

SERVES 6

CALORIES PER SERVING: 95.2

FAT (G) PER SERVING: 0.2

Remember when your mother used to shake-and-bake everything? Growing up, I loved coming home and smelling the aroma of roasted potatoes flavoured with garlic and onion.

1 tsp garlic powder	6 medium potatoes, cut into
1/2 tsp onion powder	cubes or wedges
1/2 tsp chili powder	4 cloves garlic, cut in half
1/2 tsp dried rosemary	1 bunch chives, finely chopped
1/2 tsp black pepper	

In a large freezer bag, combine the garlic powder, onion powder, chili powder, rosemary and pepper. Add the potato wedges and shake well to coat evenly. In a non-stick baking dish, place the potatoes, garlic and chives. Bake in a preheated oven at 350°F for 25 minutes. Broil potatoes until golden, about 2 minutes.

Schedule workouts into your week. Try to exercise at least 3 times per week for at least 20 minutes.

Substitution:
- *Replace potatoes with yams or sweet potatoes.*

Chili and Garlic Roasted Potatoes

SERVES 4

CALORIES PER SERVING: 125.7

FAT (G) PER SERVING: 0.9

The Chili and Garlic Roasted Potatoes make a wonderful side dish for poultry, meat or seafood.

2 tbsp chili powder	1/2 tsp black pepper
1 tsp paprika	4 large potatoes, cut into
1 tsp dry oregano	large pieces
1 tbsp garlic powder	

Put the chili powder, paprika, oregano, garlic powder and pepper in a large freezer bag. Place the potatoes in the bag and coat with cooking spray for about 4 seconds. Shake well to ensure the potatoes are evenly coated. Place the potatoes in a non-stick baking dish or on a cookie sheet and bake in a preheated oven at 350°F for 25 minutes. Broil for 5 minutes until golden brown.

Substitution:
• Replace potatoes with cubed sweet potatoes.

Roasted Yams with Cinnamon

SERVES 4

CALORIES PER SERVING: 118.4

FAT (G) PER SERVING: 0.3

Yams have become one of my favourite side dishes to serve. When they are baked or roasted they are especially flavourful.

1/2 tsp cinnamon	1 tbsp apple juice concentrate
1/4 tsp nutmeg	1 medium apple, cored and
1/2 tsp black pepper	cut into 8 wedges
2 medium yams, cut into wedges	

In a small bowl, combine the cinnamon, nutmeg and pepper. Toss the yam wedges with apple juice concentrate so the yams become coated with the concentrate. Place the yam and apple wedges on a non-stick cookie sheet or in a small non-stick baking dish and sprinkle on the spice mixture. Bake in a preheated oven at 350°F for 30 minutes or until yams are tender. Broil for about 4 minutes, until browned.

Substitution:
- *Substitute sweet potatoes for yams.*

PASTA

Macaroni with Cheese and Ground Chicken

SERVES 8

CALORIES PER SERVING: 328.4

FAT (G) PER SERVING: 11.5

When I was growing up, we often had macaroni and cheese for dinner. Try this version, and add other ingredients.

1 tbsp canola oil	1/2 tsp dried basil
1 medium onion, chopped	1/2 tsp dried thyme
2 cloves garlic, chopped	1/2 tsp dried sage
1 medium red pepper, diced	1/2 tsp black pepper
1 lb lean ground chicken	1/2 cup non-fat sour cream
4 cups chicken stock (low-sodium/low-fat)	1/2 cup shredded low-fat cheddar cheese
2 medium tomatoes, chopped	1/2 cup chopped fresh parsley
3 cups elbow macaroni	

In a large, deep sauté pan, heat the oil and sauté the onion, garlic and red pepper about 2 minutes. Add the ground chicken and sauté 10 minutes or until chicken is cooked thoroughly. Meanwhile, heat the stock in a saucepan or in the microwave. To the chicken add the hot stock, tomatoes, macaroni, basil, thyme, sage and black pepper. Simmer 10 minutes or until stock has reduced and macaroni is cooked. Stir in the sour cream and cheese; cook on low heat another 5 minutes, stirring until creamy. Stir in parsley.

Substitutions:
- *Substitute ground turkey or lean ground beef for the chicken.*
- *Substitute non-fat yogurt for the sour cream.*

Mushroom Bow-Tie Pasta

SERVES 6

CALORIES PER SERVING: 245.1

FAT (G) PER SERVING: 2.3

You can prepare this recipe with any type of mushroom.

3 cups bow-tie pasta
1 tsp canola oil
1 small onion, chopped
2 cloves garlic, chopped
3 cups button mushrooms, chopped
2/3 cup vegetable stock (low-sodium/low-fat)

2 tbsp low-fat sour cream
2 tbsp chopped fresh basil
1 cup chopped fresh parsley
1 tsp black pepper
1/2 cup grated low-fat Parmesan cheese

In a large pot, boil 6 cups of lightly salted water. Toss in bow-tie pasta and cook for 10 minutes or until tender. Drain, rinse with cold water and set aside. Meanwhile, in a large sauté pan, heat the oil and sauté the onion and garlic 3 minutes or until translucent. Add the mushrooms and brown another 4 minutes. Stir in 1 tbsp of the stock. Reduce heat to low. Make a space in the centre of the mixture, add the sour cream and mix until smooth. Add remaining stock, the basil, 1/2 cup of the parsley and the black pepper. Gently simmer the sauce another 5 minutes or until the liquid has reduced by half. Add the cooked pasta, remaining parsley and the Parmesan cheese. Mix well and serve.

Hold all stretches for approximately 15 to 20 seconds.

Substitution:
• Substitute low-fat yogurt for the sour cream.

Vegetarian Substitution:
• Substitute low-fat rice sour cream or rice milk for sour cream.

Pasta Shells with Zucchini and Parmesan

SERVES 6

CALORIES PER SERVING: 252.7

FAT (G) PER SERVING: 2.2

Zucchini makes a wonderful base for a pasta sauce. When I want light, flavourful pasta (which is always!) I make this recipe.

2/3 cup vegetable stock (low-sodium/low-fat)

1 small onion, chopped

1 small green pepper, sliced

2 cloves garlic, chopped

1/2 cup fresh basil, chopped OR 1/2 tsp dried

2 tbsp chopped fresh sage OR 1/4 tsp dried

1 tbsp chopped fresh thyme OR 1/2 tsp dried

1/2 tsp black pepper

3 cups pasta shells

1/2 cup non-fat sour cream

1 medium zucchini, diced

1/4 cup grated low-fat Parmesan cheese

In a large sauté pan, heat 3 tbsp of the stock and gently sauté the onion, green pepper and garlic about 4 minutes. Add the remaining stock, the basil, sage, thyme and black pepper. Simmer another 5 minutes or until liquid has reduced by half. Reduce heat to low. Meanwhile, in 4 cups boiling salted water, cook the pasta until tender, about 7 minutes. Drain and rinse with cold water. Add the sour cream to the sauce and mix well until smooth. Add the zucchini; simmer about 5 minutes, until zucchini is cooked. Add the Parmesan cheese and the cooked pasta shells. Mix well and serve.

Stretch to the limit of movement, not to the point of pain.

Penne with Fresh Herbs, Mushrooms and Tomatoes

SERVES 6

CALORIES PER SERVING: 230.6

FAT (G) PER SERVING: 1.2

Quite often I serve a very large bowl of pasta as a main dish with salad and bread. Occasionally I serve a small portion of pasta at the beginning of a meal, but then with the main course I don't serve another carbohydrate; I have the main course and two vegetables along with a fresh light salad.

3 cups penne
1 1/2 cups vegetable stock (low-sodium/low-fat)
1 medium onion, chopped
2 cups chopped button mushrooms
1/2 cup chopped fresh basil OR 1/2 tsp dried

1/4 cup chopped fresh oregano OR 1/2 tsp dried
1/4 cup chopped fresh sage OR 1/4 tsp dried
1 19-oz can (low-sodium) stewed tomatoes
1/4 cup chopped fresh parsley

In a large pot, bring 4 cups water to a boil. Toss in penne and cook for 10 minutes or until tender. Drain, rinse and set aside. In a large frying pan or wok, heat stock. Add onion, mushrooms, basil, oregano, sage and tomatoes; simmer 12 to 15 minutes or until liquid has reduced by half. Add penne and mix well. Garnish with parsley and serve.

Substitutions:
• Replace the herbs with others such as rosemary, tarragon or thyme.
• Replace the button mushrooms with Portobello or shiitake and you will have more flavour.
• Replace the vegetable stock with low-sodium chicken stock.

Penne with Roasted Vegetables

SERVES 6

CALORIES PER SERVING: 255.2

FAT (G) PER SERVING: 1.8

This pasta recipe comes in handy a day or two after I have a barbecue with grilled vegetables served as a side dish. It's a great way to use leftovers.

1 medium red onion, cubed
1 small zucchini, cubed
1 medium red pepper, cut in half
1 medium green pepper, cut in half
1 cup button mushrooms
1 cup broccoli florets
1 tsp garlic powder
1/2 tsp dried rosemary
1/2 tsp dried oregano
1/2 tsp paprika
3 cups penne
1/2 cup vegetable stock (low-sodium/low-fat)
1/4 cup apple juice
1/2 tsp dried basil
1/2 tsp black pepper
1/2 cup chopped fresh parsley
1/4 cup grated low-fat Parmesan cheese

In a non-stick roasting pan, combine the onion, zucchini, red pepper, green pepper, mushrooms and broccoli. Sprinkle with the garlic powder, rosemary, oregano and paprika; toss well. Cook pasta in 4 cups lightly salted boiling water for about 8 minutes; drain, rinse and set aside. Meanwhile, broil vegetables about 5 minutes. Turn and broil another 2 minutes. In a large sauté pan, simmer the stock, apple juice, basil and black pepper. Stir in the roasted vegetables, pasta and parsley. Heat another 2 minutes and then add the Parmesan cheese. Mix well and serve.

Substitution:
• Substitute any other vegetables you have or prefer.

Rigatoni with Pesto and Fresh Vegetables

SERVES 6

CALORIES PER SERVING: 364.5

FAT (G) PER SERVING: 23.5

Quite often I serve a small portion of pasta with pesto and I use what vegetables I have to complete this dish.

1 1/2 cups chopped fresh basil	1 tbsp balsamic vinegar
1/2 cup canola oil	1/2 tsp black pepper
1/4 cup pine nuts	2 cups rigatoni
2 cloves garlic (optional)	1/2 red pepper, chopped
1/2 cup grated low-fat Parmesan cheese	1/2 cup button mushrooms, chopped
	1/2 cup cubed zucchini

In a food processor, combine the basil, oil, pine nuts, garlic (if using), 1/4 cup of the Parmesan, the balsamic vinegar and black pepper. Purée. Cook the rigatoni in lightly salted boiling water until tender, about 7 minutes. In the last 2 minutes, add the red pepper, mushrooms and zucchini. Reserve some of the cooking water and drain the pasta and vegetables. Add the pesto and mix while warm. If the pesto is too thick, add some of the pasta water to thin out. Sprinkle with remaining Parmesan.

Make sure to stretch opposing muscle groups equally.

Substitutions:
- Substitute 1/4 cup olive oil for 1/4 cup of canola oil.
- For milder flavour, substitute 1 small shallot or onion for garlic.
- Substitute more flavourful Portobello or shiitake mushrooms for button mushrooms.

Rotini with Beef Tenderloin and Basil

SERVES 6

CALORIES PER SERVING: 324.7

FAT (G) PER SERVING: 7.3

This combination of beef with pasta and basil is a real treat. I first experienced a version of this recipe in Venice a few years ago.

3 cups rotini
1 tbsp canola oil
1 medium red onion, sliced
2 cloves garlic, chopped
2 6-oz tenderloin steaks, sliced
2 large tomatoes, chopped
1/2 cup chopped fresh basil OR
1 tsp dried

1/2 cup chopped fresh parsley
OR 1 tsp dried
1/2 cup beef stock (low-sodium/low-fat)
1/4 tsp sea salt
1/2 tsp black pepper

Boil the rotini in 4 cups salted water for about 7 minutes, until tender; drain well. Meanwhile, in a large sauté pan, heat the oil and sauté the onion for 2 minutes. Add the garlic and sauté another minute. Add the steak and sauté 4 minutes. Add the tomatoes, basil, parsley, stock, salt and pepper; mix well. Cook for another 5 minutes, allowing liquid to reduce by half. Add the pasta and mix well. Serve immediately.

> Several studies have found that physical activity, even at relatively low intensity levels, can play a positive role in preventing some types of cancer.

Rotini with Turkey Sausage and Sage

SERVES 6

CALORIES PER SERVING: 352.5

FAT (G) PER SERVING: 8.5

Pasta and sausage make a great combination.

4 large low-fat turkey sausages
3 cups rotini
2/3 cup chicken stock (low-sodium/low-fat)
1 small onion, chopped
1 red pepper, chopped
2 cloves garlic, chopped
2 tbsp chopped fresh basil, OR 1/2 tsp dried
1/2 tsp black pepper
1/2 tsp dried sage

Grill the turkey sausage and slice into 1-inch pieces; set aside. Boil the rotini in lightly salted water for 7 minutes or until tender. Drain, rinse with cold water and set aside. Meanwhile, in a frying pan, heat 3 tbsp of the chicken stock and sauté the onion, red pepper and garlic for 3 minutes or until onion is translucent. Add the remaining stock, the basil, black pepper and sage. Bring just to a boil. Add the sausage to the sauté pan, mix well and heat through. Serve immediately over the pasta.

Establish realistic fitness goals.

Substitution:
• Substitute either chicken or beef sausage for turkey sausage.

Vegetarian Substitution:
• Substitute the turkey sausage with 3 cups sliced Portobello mushrooms.

Fettuccine with Ham and Asparagus

SERVES 6

CALORIES PER SERVING: 258.4

FAT (G) PER SERVING: 4.4

Fettuccine with a white sauce, ham and asparagus gives a different twist to pasta.

10 oz fettuccine	1/2 cup non-fat sour cream
1 tbsp canola oil	1/2 cup non-fat or skim milk
1 small onion, chopped	1/2 tsp dried basil
2 cloves garlic, chopped	1/2 tsp black pepper
12 medium asparagus stalks, chopped	2 tbsp grated low-fat Parmesan cheese
1/2 cup cubed lean cooked ham	1/4 cup chopped fresh parsley

In a large pot, bring 4 cups slightly salted water to a boil. Toss in fettuccine and cook for about 7 minutes, stirring occasionally to prevent sticking. Drain well. Meanwhile, in a large sauté pan, heat the oil and sauté the onion and garlic about 2 minutes. Add the asparagus and sauté another minute. Stir in the ham. Reduce heat to medium and add the sour cream and milk. Stir gently for 3 minutes or until smooth. Add the basil and black pepper. Simmer another 5 minutes and then toss in the fettuccine. Add the Parmesan and mix well. Garnish with fresh parsley.

Wearing heavier outfits during exercise does not make you burn more fat—it only causes you to lose water.

Substitution:
• Substitute 1 1/2 cups chopped mushrooms for the ham.

Spaghetti with Clams, Zucchini and Red Pepper

SERVES 6

CALORIES PER SERVING: 385.8

FAT (G) PER SERVING: 2.1

Pasta is a staple in much of the Mediterranean, not only in Italy. You will find it in Greece, Malta, Spain and the northern coast of Africa. The wonderful thing about pasta is that it can be combined with almost any ingredient from your supermarket.

1/2 cup vegetable stock (low-sodium/low-fat)	1 large red pepper, chopped
2 cloves garlic, minced	1/4 cup chopped fresh basil OR 1/2 tsp dried
1 medium onion, chopped	1/4 cup chopped fresh oregano
1 19-oz can stewed tomatoes	OR 1/2 tsp dried
1 14-oz can clams, drained and rinsed	1/2 tsp black pepper
1 medium zucchini, cubed (about 1 cup)	18 oz spaghetti

In a large sauté pan or wok, combine the stock, garlic and onion. Gently sauté 2 to 3 minutes. Add the tomatoes, clams, zucchini, red pepper, half of the basil and oregano, and the black pepper. Simmer for 10 minutes or until liquid has reduced by half. If the liquid reduces too much, add some more vegetable stock. Meanwhile, cook the spaghetti in 6 cups of boiling water for 8 minutes or until tender. Drain, rinse with cold water and set aside. To the sauce add the remaining basil and oregano and the spaghetti. Mix well in and serve immediately.

Substitutions:
• Sauté with cooking spray instead of stock.
• Add 1/4 cup red wine to the sauce while simmering—this will add a rich, hearty flavour.

Spaghetti with Tomatoes and Fresh Basil

SERVES 6

CALORIES PER SERVING: 388.9

FAT (G) PER SERVING: 2.3

Simplicity is the best way to describe this recipe. Just take some basic ingredients and make a wonderful meal.

18 oz spaghetti
1/2 cup vegetable stock (low-sodium/low-fat)
1 medium onion, chopped
2 cloves garlic, chopped
1 small green pepper, chopped
1 28-oz can diced tomatoes
1/2 cup dry red wine

1/2 tsp dried oregano
1/2 tsp chili powder
1/2 tsp black pepper
1/2 cup chopped fresh basil
1/2 cup chopped fresh parsley
1/4 cup grated low-fat Parmesan cheese

Cook the spaghetti in 6 cups of boiling water for 8 minutes or until tender. Drain, rinse with cold water and set aside. Meanwhile, in a large sauté pan, heat the stock and sauté the onion, garlic and green pepper about 5 minutes. Add the tomatoes, wine, oregano, chili powder and black pepper. Cook for another 5 minutes. Stir in the basil and parsley. Cook another 5 minutes. Pour the sauce over the spaghetti and sprinkle with Parmesan cheese.

Exercise should not be viewed as a contest. When you exercise properly, there are no losers—only winners.

Substitution:
• Substitute 2 tbsp canola oil for the soup stock.

Tri-colour Fusilli with Goat Cheese

SERVES 6

CALORIES PER SERVING: 258.1

FAT (G) PER SERVING: 5.4

The goat cheese adds texture to this pasta sauce.

3 cups tri-colour fusilli
1 tbsp canola oil
1 small onion, chopped
2 cloves garlic, chopped
1/2 cup button mushrooms, chopped
1 small red pepper, chopped
1/2 cup vegetable stock (low-sodium/low-fat)

2 tbsp chopped fresh basil,
   OR 1/2 tsp dried
1 tbsp chopped fresh oregano,
   OR 1/4 tsp dried
1/2 tsp black pepper
1/4 cup mild soft goat cheese

Cook the pasta in 4 cups of boiling, slightly salted water for 8 minutes or until tender. Drain, rinse with cold water and set aside. Meanwhile in a skillet or frying pan, heat the oil and sauté the onion for 2 minutes or until translucent. Add the garlic, mushrooms and red pepper. Cook another 3 minutes. Add the stock, basil, oregano and black pepper; cook another 2 minutes. Add the goat cheese and stir until smooth. Add the pasta and mix well. Serve immediately.

Substitution:
• Substitute low-fat cream cheese for the goat cheese.

Tri-colour Fusilli with Turkey Bacon and Tomatoes

SERVES 6

CALORIES PER SERVING: 241.7

FAT (G) PER SERVING: 1.5

The Tri-colour Fusilli with Turkey Bacon and Tomatoes is one of my favourite dishes to serve as a starter. Turkey bacon is readily available in your local supermarkets and usually contains 30% to 50% less fat than regular bacon. The secret to this recipe is the apple juice, which adds a slight sweetness to the sauce.

1 cup apple juice	1/2 tsp dried basil
1/2 lb turkey bacon, chopped	1/2 tsp dried sage
1 medium red onion, chopped	1/2 tsp chili powder
2 cloves garlic, chopped	1/2 tsp black pepper
1 green pepper, chopped	3 cups tri-colour fusilli
1 28-oz can stewed tomatoes	

In a large, deep non-stick frying pan over medium heat, heat 1/2 cup of the apple juice; gently brown the bacon for about 4 minutes. Add the onion, garlic and green pepper; sauté another 4 minutes. Then add the tomatoes, basil, sage, chili powder, black pepper and remaining apple juice. Simmer about 10 minutes, until the liquid has reduced by one-third. Meanwhile, cook fusilli in 6 cups of boiling water for 7 to 8 minutes, or until al dente. Drain and rinse with cold water. Add sauce to pasta, mix well and serve immediately.

TIP

I like to rinse the pasta under cold water to stop the cooking and remove excess starch. If the sauté pan is big enough, add the pasta to the sauce and mix well in the pan. If not, pour over pasta in a large bowl and then mix.

Substitutions:
- Substitute chicken bacon for the turkey bacon.
- Substitute 1 cup dry white wine for the apple juice.

Vegetable Herb Lasagna

SERVES 6

CALORIES PER SERVING: 364.4

FAT (G) PER SERVING: 5.4

The Vegetable Herb Lasagna is a starter I had in the Lake Como area of northern Italy. I have changed a few ingredients but kept it true to the region. It's a good main course or lunch with a light salad.

2 tbsp vegetable stock (low-sodium/low-fat)
1 medium onion, sliced
1/2 cup grated carrot
1 cup sliced mushrooms
1 red pepper, sliced
1 cup sliced broccoli
1/4 cup chopped fresh basil
1 tbsp chopped fresh rosemary
1 tbsp chopped fresh oregano
1/2 tsp black pepper
1 19-oz can crushed tomatoes
1 tsp tomato paste
1/2 tsp chili powder
12 cooked lasagna noodles
1 cup low-fat cottage cheese OR ricotta
1/2 cup shredded low-fat mozzarella cheese

In a non-stick frying pan, heat 2 tbsp of the stock and sauté the onion, carrot, mushrooms, red pepper and broccoli about 2 minutes. Add the basil, rosemary, oregano and black pepper. In a saucepan over medium heat, combine the tomatoes, tomato paste and chili powder. Simmer for about 5 minutes. Spray an 8- x 8-inch baking dish with cooking spray. Spread some tomato sauce on the bottom, then cover with a layer of noodles, one-third of the vegetable and herb mixture, one-third of the cottage cheese and 1/2 cup of the tomato sauce. Repeat the layers, ending with a layer of noodles and the remaining sauce. Sprinkle with the mozzarella cheese. Bake in a preheated oven at 350°F about 25 minutes or until brown on top. Let stand about 10 minutes before serving.

Mediterranean Seafood Lasagna

SERVES 8 TO 10

CALORIES PER SERVING: 348.6–278.9

FAT (G) PER SERVING: 6.9–5.5

My previous version of this seafood lasagna was a huge hit. Try this low-fat version.

1 28-oz can crushed tomatoes

1/2 tsp onion powder

1/2 tsp garlic powder

1/2 tsp dried basil

1/2 tsp dried thyme

1/2 tsp dried oregano

1/2 tsp black pepper

1/2 cup chopped fresh parsley

1/2 cup canned clams, drained and rinsed

1 cup small shrimp, peeled and deveined

1/2 cup crabmeat

1 medium red pepper, chopped

1 medium green pepper, chopped

1/2 cup grated carrot

1/4 cup lemon juice

10–12 cooked lasagna noodles

3/4 cup shredded low-fat mozzarella cheese

1/4 cup grated Parmesan cheese

1/4 cup shredded low-fat cheddar cheese

In a saucepan, combine the tomatoes, onion powder, garlic powder, basil, thyme, oregano and black pepper. Mix well and simmer for 10 minutes. Meanwhile, in a mixing bowl, combine the parsley, clams, shrimp, crabmeat, red and green peppers, carrot and lemon juice. Gently mix. In a 13- x 9-inch baking dish, place a layer of lasagna noodles, some sauce, some seafood mixture and then some of the mozzarella cheese. Continue layering, ending with a layer of noodles. Top with the Parmesan and cheddar cheese. Bake in a preheated oven at 350°F for 25 minutes or until top starts to turn golden.

Substitution:
• Substitute scallops, tuna or swordfish for the crab or shrimp.

VEGETARIAN

Baked Couscous with Chick Peas and Mushrooms

SERVES 6

CALORIES PER SERVING: 213.8

FAT (G) PER SERVING: 1.7

I was introduced to couscous in the Middle East years ago. I serve it in a variety of recipes with whatever ingredients I have available.

1 1/2 cups vegetable stock (low-sodium/low-fat)

1 cup couscous

1 small onion, chopped

2 cloves garlic, chopped

1 cup chopped button mushrooms

1 cup canned chick peas, drained

2 small tomatoes, chopped

1 tsp chili powder

1 tsp Dijon mustard

1/2 tsp dried rosemary

1/2 tsp black pepper

1/2 cup dry red wine

1/2 cup chopped fresh parsley

1/4 cup grated low-fat Parmesan cheese

Heat the stock in the microwave until boiling, then pour into a deep baking dish. Add the couscous, onion, garlic, mushrooms, chick peas, tomatoes, chili powder, mustard, rosemary, pepper and wine. Mix well and bake in a preheated oven at 350°F for 15 minutes. Mix in the parsley and top with the Parmesan cheese. Bake for another 5 minutes or until golden.

Strengthening and toning your abdominals helps prevent back pain and aids in posture.

Substitution:
• *Substitute 2 cups cooked rice for the couscous.*

Vegetable Risotto

SERVES 4

CALORIES PER SERVING: 274.8

FAT (G) PER SERVING: 3.0

Risotto is one of my favourite dishes and this one, mixed with fresh vegetables, is a treat. Risotto is not that difficult to prepare; you just need patience and the finished product will be worth it.

6 cups vegetable stock (low-sodium/low-fat)
1 medium red onion, chopped
2 cloves garlic, chopped
2 cups arborio rice
2 medium plum tomatoes, chopped
2 medium carrots, chopped
10 asparagus stalks, chopped
1/2 cup button mushrooms, chopped
1/2 tsp dried basil
1/2 tsp dried thyme
1/2 tsp chili powder
1 bay leaf
1 tbsp calorie-reduced margarine
1/4 cup grated low-fat Parmesan cheese

In a large pot, bring the stock to a boil; reduce to simmer. In a separate soup pot or a large non-stick saucepan, place 1/4 cup of the stock and sauté the onion and garlic for 2 minutes or until onion is translucent. Add the rice and stir well. Using a ladle, add just enough stock to cover the rice. Stir until stock is absorbed. Continue ladling stock, 1 cup at a time, into pot for about 10 minutes, stirring constantly and letting stock absorb before adding more. Add the tomatoes, carrots, asparagus, mushrooms, basil, thyme, chili powder and bay leaf; stir well. Add more stock and stir for another 5 minutes or until the rice becomes moist and creamy. Remove the bay leaf. Stir in the margarine and Parmesan; serve immediately.

Try an aquafit class—it is easy on the joints and lots of fun.

Mushroom and Herb Risotto

SERVES 4

CALORIES PER SERVING: 338.5

FAT (G) PER SERVING: 5.8

The Mushroom and Herb Risotto recipe calls for tofu and a calorie-reduced margarine—I add to the flavour with a selection of herbs and spices.

5 cups vegetable stock (low-sodium/low-fat)

1 tsp canola oil

1 medium red onion, chopped

2 cloves garlic, finely chopped

2 cups arborio rice

1 cup button mushrooms, sliced

1 cup sliced Portobello mushrooms

1 cup shiitake mushrooms, sliced

1 tbsp chopped fresh rosemary, OR 1/2 tsp dried

1 tbsp chopped fresh thyme, OR 1/2 tsp dried

1/2 tsp chili powder

1/2 tsp black pepper

1 bay leaf

1/2 cup dry red wine

1 tbsp calorie-reduced margarine

1/2 cup low-fat soft tofu

In a large pot, bring the stock to a boil; reduce to simmer. In a large, deep saucepan, heat the oil. Toss in the onion and garlic and gently sauté until onion is translucent. Add the rice and sauté, stirring about 2 minutes. Add the mushrooms and sauté another 2 minutes. Using a ladle, add enough stock to just cover the rice. Cook, stirring, about 10 minutes or until stock is absorbed. Add the rosemary, thyme, chili powder, pepper, bay leaf and wine. Continue stirring, adding stock 1 cup at a time, letting stock absorb before adding more. Once the risotto starts to become creamy, remove the bay leaf and add the margarine and tofu. Serve immediately.

Exercise helps to improve flexibility and muscle strength to help prevent falls and fractures.

Substitution:
- *Use all one kind of mushroom, or a mixture.*

Grilled Portobello Mushrooms with Sweet Onion Relish

SERVES 4

CALORIES PER SERVING: 112.5

FAT (G) PER SERVING: 4.7

Portobello mushrooms, when grilled, take on a meaty texture. As a side dish, prepare garlic mashed potatoes with some fresh herbs such as oregano and parsley.

8 Portobello mushrooms, stems removed	1/2 tsp dried sage
4 tbsp canola oil	1/2 tsp black pepper
1/2 tsp garlic powder	1 medium onion, cut into thin rings
1/2 tsp onion powder	3/4 cup apple juice
1/2 tsp paprika	1 tbsp liquid honey
1/2 tsp dried basil	1/2 small red pepper, diced

Using a paper towel, gently clean off the tops of the Portobello mushrooms and brush with 3 tsp of the canola oil. In a small bowl, combine the garlic powder, onion powder, paprika, basil, sage and black pepper. Mix together and sprinkle evenly on the tops of the mushrooms. Let sit about 2 minutes before grilling. Start to grill the bottoms first, about 2 minutes. Turn over and grill about 5 minutes or until grill marks appear. To prepare the relish, in a small saucepan, heat the remaining oil and gently sauté the onion about 3 minutes. Add the apple juice, honey and red pepper. Cook another 4 minutes or until liquid is reduced by half. Serve the onion relish on top of the Portobello mushrooms.

Substitution:
• Substitute thickly sliced eggplant for the Portobello mushrooms. Grill about the same time but sprinkle the herb mixture on both sides.

Spinach and Mushroom Pie

SERVES 4

CALORIES PER SERVING: 317.5

FAT (G) PER SERVING: 18.8

This pie also makes a great choice for brunch.

2 tbsp canola oil

1 small onion, chopped

2 cups chopped button mushrooms

1/2 cup vegetable stock (low-sodium/low-fat)

2 lb spinach, chopped

1 medium carrot, grated

1 cup chopped fresh parsley

1/4 cup chopped fresh dill

1/2 tsp dried thyme

1/2 tsp black pepper

1/2 cup shredded low-fat cheddar cheese

2 tbsp non-fat sour cream

1 unbaked 9-inch pie crust

In a large sauté pan, heat oil. Toss in onion and mushrooms and sauté for 3 to 4 minutes. Add the stock. Add the spinach in handfuls. Cook about 5 minutes or until the spinach starts to wilt and liquid has reduced. Remove from heat. Add the carrot, parsley, dill, thyme, pepper, cheese and sour cream. Mix well and spoon into the pie crust. Bake in a preheated oven at 350°F for 25 minutes or until the crust is cooked and golden.

Go for a stroll during lunch or coffee breaks.

Substitution:
• Replace button mushrooms with a combination of Portobello, shiitake and oyster—this adds a wild flavour!

Baked Fennel with Mustard Sauce

SERVES 6

CALORIES PER SERVING: 109.7

FAT (G) PER SERVING: 1.6

As you know, I love fennel, and baking it as a main dish or preparing less as a side dish will have your guests asking for the recipe.

6 medium fennel bulbs, cut into slices
1 medium onion, cut into rings
1/2 tsp dried tarragon
1 tsp black pepper
1/4 cup grated low-fat Parmesan cheese

1/2 cup vegetable stock (low-sodium/low-fat)
1/2 cup non-fat sour cream
3 tbsp Dijon mustard
1/2 tsp dried thyme

In a large pot, bring 6 cups of water to a boil. Toss in fennel and blanch for 5 minutes. Remove fennel and place in a baking dish. Cover with the onion, tarragon and 1/2 tsp of the pepper. Sprinkle with the Parmesan and bake in a preheated oven of 350°F for 20 minutes. The fennel should have a golden colour from the cheese. Meanwhile, in a small saucepan, combine the stock, sour cream and mustard. Heat to almost a boil while whisking mixture smooth, about 4 minutes. Add the dried thyme and remaining pepper. Whisk another 4 minutes. Serve fennel with sauce.

Examples of household activities that burn fat are cleaning windows, washing the car, raking the yard, walking the dog and gardening.

Substitution:
• Substitute non-fat yogurt for the sour cream; mix longer until smooth.

Baked Zucchini with Tomatoes and Fresh Basil

SERVES 6

CALORIES PER SERVING: 119.5

FAT (G) PER SERVING: 3.9

Zucchini comes in green and yellow and can be baked, grilled or stewed. In this recipe, I bake the zucchini and smother it with a wonderful tomato-basil sauce.

1 tsp black pepper

1 tsp chili powder

1 tsp paprika

1/2 tsp dried thyme

1/2 tsp dried rosemary

1/2 tsp dried mint

1/2 tsp onion powder

1/2 tsp garlic powder

6 medium zucchini (3 yellow/ 3 green), sliced

1 28-oz can diced stewed tomatoes

1 small green pepper, chopped

1/2 cup chopped fresh basil

1/2 cup crumbled light feta cheese

In a bowl, combine 1/2 tsp of the black pepper, 1/2 tsp of the chili powder, the paprika, thyme, rosemary, mint, onion powder and garlic powder; mix well. Coat the sliced zucchini in the mixture and place in a 9-inch baking dish. Bake in a preheated oven at 350°F for 20 minutes or until tender. In a small saucepan, combine the tomatoes, green pepper, basil and remaining chili powder and black pepper. Simmer for about 1 minute and pour over the baked zucchini. Sprinkle feta over the zucchini and sauce.

Decide what you will do to achieve your goals.

Substitutions:
• Substitute a white sauce or pesto sauce for the tomato sauce.
• Substitute 1/2 cup finely chopped olives for the green peppers.

Roasted Eggplant with Tomatoes and Green Peppers

SERVES 8

CALORIES PER SERVING: 78.9

FAT (G) PER SERVING: 0.5

The combination of the eggplant, tomatoes and fresh basil makes a tantalizing main meal. You can add other vegetables if you like.

1 medium eggplant, cut in 1-inch cubes (about 4 cups)
1 28-oz can low-sodium stewed tomatoes (no sugar added)
4 green peppers, chopped
1 medium red onion, chopped

2 cloves garlic, chopped
1 cup parsley, chopped
1/2 cup grated carrot
1/4 cup chopped fresh basil OR 1 tsp dried
1/2 tsp black pepper

In a large salad bowl or mixing bowl, combine eggplant, tomatoes, peppers, onion, garlic, parsley, carrot, basil and black pepper. Mix well. Transfer to a large baking dish and bake in a preheated oven at 350°F for 20 minutes, until the eggplant is tender but not mushy. Serve warm.

Exercise generates a period of substantial emotional and physical relaxation that sets in approximately an hour and a half after a relatively intense bout of physical activity.

Substitution:
• Substitute zucchini for the eggplant.

Grilled Vegetable Kabobs with Fresh Herbs and Apple

SERVES 6

CALORIES PER SERVING: 101.7

FAT (G) PER SERVING: 0.8

These vegetable kabobs make a great main dish.

6 8-inch wooden skewers
1 medium zucchini, cubed
1 green pepper, chopped into large pieces
1 red pepper, chopped into large pieces
20 large button mushrooms
1 medium red onion, cut into wedges
1/2 bunch broccoli, cut into florets

1/2 head cauliflower, coarsely chopped
2 large apples, cored and cubed
1/2 cup apple juice
1 tbsp chopped fresh rosemary OR 1/2 tsp dried
1 tbsp chopped fresh oregano OR 1/2 tsp dried
1 tsp cinnamon

Soak skewers in water for 20 minutes. Place the zucchini, peppers, mushrooms, onion, broccoli, cauliflower, apple and apple juice in a large bowl. Sprinkle with rosemary, oregano and 1/2 tsp of the cinnamon. Mix well and then add the remaining cinnamon. Thread the vegetables and apple onto skewers and grill about 8 to 10 minutes, occasionally turning to obtain grill marks.

Avoid strenuous swim workouts in heated pools during the summer.

Savoury Butternut Squash Stew with Maple Syrup and Cinnamon

SERVES 8

CALORIES PER SERVING: 163.7

FAT (G) PER SERVING: 1.7

My favourite squash is butternut, and I make this stew year round.

2 cups vegetable stock (low-sodium/low-fat)
1 cup apple juice
1/2 tsp dried basil
1/2 tsp dried rosemary
1/2 tsp black pepper
1/4 tsp dried mint
1/4 tsp dried tarragon
3 cups cubed butternut squash

2 medium potatoes, cubed
1 medium yam, peeled and cubed
2 medium carrots, cubed
1 green pepper, chopped
1 cup broccoli florets
1/2 cup frozen corn
1/2 cup maple syrup
1/2 tsp cinnamon

In a large crock pot or soup pot, combine the vegetable stock, apple juice, basil, rosemary, black pepper, mint and tarragon; bring to a boil. Reduce to a simmer and add the squash, potatoes, yam and carrots. Simmer 15 minutes. Then add the green pepper, broccoli and corn. Simmer 5 minutes. Stir in the maple syrup and cinnamon. Simmer another 5 minutes.

Consume a small amount of fluid while exercising, at least every 15 or 20 minutes.

Substitution:
• *Substitute 2 cups cubed cooked turkey for the butternut squash.*

Spicy Vegetable and Fruit Mixture with Tofu

SERVES 8

CALORIES PER SERVING: 169.2

FAT (G) PER SERVING: 1.7

The combination of fruit and vegetables with herbs makes a hearty vegetarian meal.

1 1/2 cups vegetable stock (low-sodium/low-fat)

1/2 tsp black pepper

1/2 tsp dried mint

1/2 tsp dried basil

1/2 tsp cinnamon

1/2 tsp cayenne

1/4 tsp dried sage

1/4 tsp nutmeg

2 medium potatoes, cubed

2 medium carrots, diced

1 1/2 cups apple juice

1 block firm tofu, cubed

1/2 head cauliflower, cut into pieces

1/2 bunch broccoli, cut into florets

1 medium zucchini, diced

2 medium firm tomatoes, chopped

2 apples, cored and diced

2 Bartlett pears, cored and diced

1/2 cup raisins

1/2 cup chopped fresh parsley

In a large soup pot, combine the stock, pepper, mint, basil, cinnamon, cayenne, sage and nutmeg; bring to a boil. Reduce to simmer and add the potatoes and carrots. Simmer about 10 minutes. Add the apple juice, tofu, cauliflower, broccoli, zucchini, tomatoes, apples, pears and raisins. Stir well and simmer another 10 minutes. Garnish with fresh parsley and serve.

Substitution:
• Substitute 2 cups of cubed cooked chicken for the tofu.

Spicy Vegetable Paella

SERVES 8

CALORIES PER SERVING: 169.8

FAT (G) PER SERVING: 1.3

Paella is a famous Spanish dish that allows you to combine different ingredients—whatever you have available. This is a flavourful, and popular, vegetarian version.

1 tsp canola oil	1 tsp chili powder
1/2 cup chopped onion	1/2 tsp cayenne OR hot pepper flakes
2 cloves garlic, chopped	1/2 tsp dried basil
1 red pepper, chopped	1/2 tsp dried oregano
1 green pepper, chopped	1/2 tsp black pepper
1/2 cup chopped celery	1 1/2 cups rice
1/2 cup chopped fennel	2 medium tomatoes, chopped
4 cups vegetable stock (low-sodium/low-fat)	1 medium zucchini, chopped
	1 cup chopped mushrooms

In a large soup pot, heat the oil and sauté the onion and garlic 2 minutes or until the onion is translucent. Add the peppers, celery and fennel. Sauté another 4 minutes. Add the stock, chili powder, cayenne, basil, oregano and black pepper. Bring to a boil and then add the rice, tomatoes, zucchini and mushrooms. Reduce heat and simmer, covered, another 15 minutes or until the rice has fluffed. Serve immediately.

Avoid strenuous exercise in high temperatures.

Substitution:
• Replace the soup stock with apple juice and add 2 apples for a different flavour.

Vegetable Stew with Red Wine and Herbs

SERVES 8

CALORIES PER SERVING: 120

FAT (G) PER SERVING: 0.6

This has to be one of the easiest recipes in this book: just combine the ingredients and cook!

1 19-oz can diced tomatoes
2 cups vegetable stock (low-sodium/low-fat)
1/2 tsp dried mint
1/2 tsp dried basil
1/2 tsp dried oregano
1/2 tsp chili powder
1/2 tsp black pepper
1 bay leaf
1/2 head cauliflower, coarsely chopped

1/2 bunch broccoli, cut into florets
1 medium red onion, cut into wedges
2 cloves garlic, chopped
1 medium zucchini, cut into rings
2 medium carrots, cut into chunks
2 medium potatoes, cubed
1 small sweet potato, peeled and cubed
1 cup frozen corn
1/2 cup dry red wine

In a large soup pot, combine the tomatoes and stock. Bring to a boil. Add the mint, basil, oregano, chili powder, pepper and bay leaf; reduce to simmer and stir well. Toss in the cauliflower, broccoli, onion, garlic, zucchini, carrots, potatoes, sweet potato and corn. Simmer for 15 minutes. Add the red wine and simmer another 10 minutes or until the vegetables are tender and liquid has reduced by half. Remove the bay leaf.

Substitution:
• Use any other vegetables or amounts.

Stir-Fried Cabbage and Apple

SERVES 6

CALORIES PER SERVING: 112.8

FAT (G) PER SERVING: 0.9

This stir-fried cabbage dish is a main meal that your family will love.

1 cup vegetable stock (low-sodium/low-fat)

1 medium onion, chopped

2 cloves garlic, chopped

1 large carrot, grated

1 red pepper, chopped

1 small zucchini, grated

1/2 tsp dried basil

1/2 tsp dried thyme

1 large head green cabbage, cored and chopped

1/2 cup apple juice

3 apples, cored and chopped

1/2 tsp cinnamon

1/4 tsp nutmeg

In a large sauté pan, heat 1/2 cup of the stock and sauté the onion, garlic, carrot, red pepper and zucchini about 4 minutes. Add remaining stock, basil, thyme and the cabbage in handfuls. Sauté about 15 minutes. Add the apple juice, apples, cinnamon and nutmeg. Mix well and sauté, stirring, another 5 minutes.

To stay on track with exercise, make it convenient. Keep your gym bag close by.

Substitution:
- *Substitute firm pears for apples and use pear nectar.*

Vegetarian Cabbage Rolls

MAKES 12 TO 16 CABBAGE ROLLS

CALORIES PER SERVING: 256

FAT (G) PER SERVING: 1.4

When I was growing up, we had cabbage rolls about every two weeks. This is my updated version, which I think you'll enjoy.

1 large head green cabbage, cored
3 cups cooked rice
2 cups finely chopped celery
1 cup chopped button mushrooms
1/2 cup grated carrot
1 small red pepper, finely chopped
1 small green pepper, finely chopped
1 small onion, finely chopped

2 cloves garlic, finely chopped
2 medium tomatoes, finely chopped
1 cup chopped fresh parsley
1/4 cup chopped fresh basil
1 tsp black pepper
1 19-oz can stewed tomatoes, chopped

In a large pot, bring 6 cups of water to a boil. Toss in head of cabbage and blanch for 4 minutes. Allow to cool, then remove the leaves whole. Meanwhile, in a small bowl, combine the rice, celery, mushrooms, carrot, peppers, onion, garlic, fresh tomatoes, parsley, half of the basil and 1/2 tsp of the black pepper; mix well. Distribute mixture on the leaves in a line down the centre; tuck ends in. Gently roll edges of each leaf and place rolls in casserole or baking dish. Top with the stewed tomatoes and the remaining basil and pepper. Bake in a preheated oven at 350°F for 25 minutes.

Make a commitment and follow the regimen.

SEAFOOD

Halibut with a Vegetable Relish

SERVES 4

CALORIES PER SERVING: 151.1

FAT (G) PER SERVING: 2.4

You can usually purchase halibut fresh or frozen at your local supermarket year round. When making a vegetable relish, you can always substitute other vegetables you have in your refrigerator. The relish can also be served cold.

1/4 cup apple juice	1 small red onion, chopped
2 large halibut fillets, cut in half OR 4 medium fillets	2 cloves garlic, chopped
	1/2 cup chopped fennel
2 tbsp lemon juice	1 carrot, chopped
1/4 cup chopped fresh mint OR 1/4 tsp dried	1 medium red pepper, chopped
	2 tsp chopped fresh dill
1/2 tsp black pepper	OR 1/2 tsp dried
1/4 cup vegetable stock (low-sodium/low-fat)	1/4 tsp chili powder (optional)

Pour apple juice into a baking dish just large enough to hold the fish. Add the halibut. Cover the fish with the lemon juice, half of the mint and the black pepper. Bake in a preheated oven at 350°F for 15 minutes or until fish is white and tender. Meanwhile, to prepare the relish, heat the stock in a saucepan on medium heat and sauté the onion, garlic, fennel and carrot for 3 minutes or until the onion is translucent. Add the red pepper, the remaining mint, the dill and chili powder (if using). Sauté another 2 minutes or until the vegetables are tender. Serve the relish on top of the fish.

Skipping strengthens the legs and improves joint mobility in the hips.

Substitution:
• Substitute sole for halibut. Just make sure the sole are large pieces and bake for only 10 minutes.

Baked Halibut with Fennel and Red Pepper Relish

SERVES 4

CALORIES PER SERVING: 278.2

FAT (G) PER SERVING: 4.3

Halibut is one of my favourite dinner fish because it's so flavourful and available year round.

2 tbsp lemon juice	1/4 cup chopped fresh mint
1 small red onion, chopped	OR 1 tsp dried
1 medium red pepper, chopped	1/4 cup apple juice
1 fennel bulb, chopped (about 2 cups)	1/4 cup apple juice concentrate
1/4 cup chopped fresh dill OR	1/2 tsp black pepper
1/2 tsp dried	4 6-oz halibut fillets

In a medium mixing bowl, combine the lemon juice, onion, red pepper, fennel, dill, mint, apple juice, apple juice concentrate and black pepper. Mix well. Place the halibut on a baking sheet. Spread the relish evenly on top. Bake in a preheated oven at 350°F for 25 minutes or until fish is cooked through.

Researchers have found that people who exercise fall asleep easily, sleep more soundly and are more refreshed when they wake than those who do not exercise.

Cod with Tomatoes, Basil and Onion

SERVES 4

CALORIES PER SERVING: 87.3

FAT (G) PER SERVING: 0.6

Cod, available either fresh or frozen, can be baked, sautéed or poached.

1 19-oz can stewed tomatoes
1 medium red onion, sliced
1 green pepper, sliced
1/2 cup chopped fresh basil OR
1 tsp dried
1/2 cup chopped fresh parsley OR
1 tsp dried

1/2 tsp black pepper
1/4 tsp sea salt
1/4 tsp chili powder
1/4 tsp garlic powder
4 large cod fillets

In a large, deep sauté pan, combine the tomatoes, onion, green pepper, basil, parsley, black pepper, salt, chili powder and garlic powder. Mix well and cook on high for 3 minutes. Add the fish, reduce heat and cook another 8 to 10 minutes or until fish has turned white. Transfer fish to plates, pour sauce over fish and garnish with chopped red onion and green pepper.

TIP

To bake, combine all the ingredients except fish in a large baking dish. Place fish on top. Bake for 15 minutes at 350°F.

Substitution:
• Substitute red snapper fillets for the cod.

Crabmeat-Stuffed Cod with Mustard and Capers

SERVES 4

CALORIES PER SERVING: 262.6

FAT (G) PER SERVING: 4.5

This stuffed cod is one of my favourite recipes. If you prefer, use mushrooms, asparagus or peppers as stuffing.

1 cup canned crabmeat	1 tsp dried basil
1/2 cup finely chopped celery	1 tsp black pepper
1/2 cup finely chopped green onions	3 tbsp Dijon mustard
OR chives	4 large cod fillets
2 tsp low-fat sour cream	1/2 cup low-fat or non-fat yogurt
1 tsp balsamic vinegar	1/2 cup capers
1/4 cup shredded low-fat cheddar	

To prepare the stuffing, combine the crabmeat, celery, green onions, sour cream, balsamic vinegar, cheese, 1/2 tsp of the basil, 1/2 tsp of the pepper and 1 tbsp of the mustard. Mix well and spread on top of the cod. Roll up fish lengthwise and secure with a toothpick. Arrange cod in a small baking pan and in a preheated oven at 350°F for 20 minutes. Meanwhile, to prepare the sauce, in a small saucepan combine the yogurt and remaining mustard. Cook on medium heat until smooth. Add the capers and remaining basil and pepper. Pour the mustard and caper sauce over the fish and serve.

A properly designed exercise program will give you more energy to do the activities you enjoy and will enhance your capability to do things you like to do at home, work and play.

Stove-top Shrimp and Crabmeat Paella

SERVES 6

CALORIES PER SERVING: 333.0

FAT (G) PER SERVING: 1.6

Paella is a Spanish specialty that usually contains chicken, shrimp, sausage and some pork. This variation calls only for seafood, but don't be afraid to use up whatever meat or vegetables are in your fridge.

4 cups vegetable stock (low-sodium/low-fat)
1 medium onion, chopped
2 cloves garlic, chopped
2 celery stalks, chopped
2 medium carrots, chopped
1/4 tsp saffron
2 cups white rice
1 large red pepper, chopped
1 large green pepper, chopped
1 19-oz can low-sodium crushed or stewed tomatoes
1/2 tsp dried basil
1/2 tsp dried thyme
1/2 tsp chili powder
1/2 tsp black pepper
12 large shrimp, peeled and deveined
1 5-oz can low-sodium crabmeat, drained

In a deep sauté pan or soup pot, heat 1/4 cup of the stock. Toss in onion, garlic, celery and carrots; sauté 3 to 4 minutes or until vegetables are tender. Add the remaining stock and saffron and bring to a boil. Toss in the rice, red and green peppers, tomatoes, basil, thyme, chili powder and black pepper. Reduce heat to low and simmer about 10 minutes. Add the shrimp and crabmeat and cook until the rice is done, about another 10 minutes.

Research suggests that exercise can do for your mind what it does for your body—energize and revitalize it.

Substitution:
- *Substitute squid, swordfish or scallops for the shrimp or crabmeat.*

Creamy Shrimp Risotto

SERVES 4

CALORIES PER SERVING: 285.9

FAT (G) PER SERVING: 3.4

The first time I tasted risotto was several years ago in Venice. The secret is patience and arborio rice. Arborio rice has the ability to absorb considerable moisture without becoming soggy.

6 cups fish stock (low-sodium/low-fat)

1 medium red onion, chopped

2 cloves garlic, chopped

2 cups arborio rice

1/2 cup finely chopped parsley

1 small red pepper, chopped

2 tbsp finely chopped fresh dill

1/4 tsp dried sage

Pinch saffron

12 medium shrimp, peeled and deveined

1/2 cup non-fat sour cream

1 tbsp calorie-reduced margarine

1/4 cup grated low-fat Parmesan cheese

1/2 tsp black pepper

In a large pot, bring the stock to a boil and then reduce to a simmer. In a separate non-stick soup pot or large saucepan, place 1/4 cup of the stock and sauté the onion and garlic about 2 minutes. Add the rice and stir well. Cook about 1 minute. Using a ladle, add just enough stock to cover the rice. Stir until stock is absorbed. Continue adding stock for about 5 minutes, stirring constantly and letting stock absorb before adding more. Add the parsley, red pepper, dill and sage. Dilute the saffron in a ladle of stock and add to rice. Continue adding stock, stirring constantly, until the rice becomes moist and creamy, about 8 minutes. Add the shrimp and stir another 5 minutes or until shrimp is cooked. Add the sour cream, margarine, Parmesan and black pepper. Mix well and serve immediately.

Substitutions:
- *Substitute 12 medium scallops for the shrimp.*
- *Substitute 2 cups chopped mushrooms for the shrimp.*
- *Substitute non-fat yogurt for the sour cream.*

Poached Shrimp with Lemon, Orange and Mint

SERVES 2

CALORIES PER SERVING: 244.1

FAT (G) PER SERVING: 1.7

Shrimp is one of the most flavourful fruits of the sea and extremely popular in all parts of the Mediterranean. Poaching brings out the true flavour of seafood.

2 tbsp orange zest	1/2 tsp black pepper
1 tbsp lemon zest	1 red pepper, sliced
Juice of 1 lemon	1/2 fennel bulb, sliced (optional)
Juice of 2 oranges	12 jumbo shrimp, peeled and
1/2 cup dry white wine	deveined
1/4 cup chopped fresh mint OR	2 tbsp finely chopped fresh parsley
1/4 tsp dried	OR 1 tbsp dried

In a sauté pan or wok, combine 1 tbsp of the orange zest, the lemon zest, lemon juice, orange juice, wine, mint, black pepper, red pepper and fennel (if using); bring to a boil. Reduce to medium heat and add the shrimp. Mix well and cover for 4 to 5 minutes or until the shrimp turn pinkish-white. Remove from the poaching liquid and garnish with remaining orange zest and parsley.

Substitution:
• Replace shrimp with large sea scallops.

Shrimp and Scallops in Basil-Tomato Sauce

SERVES 4

CALORIES PER SERVING: 151.3

FAT (G) PER SERVING: 1.2

This combination of shrimp and scallops sends me to heaven. (Scallops are considered the leanest of all seafood.)

1/2 cup tomato juice

1 medium red onion, chopped

2 celery stalks, chopped

1 green pepper, chopped

2 cloves garlic, chopped

1 28-oz can crushed stewed tomatoes

1/2 cup chopped fresh basil OR 1 tsp dried

1 tbsp chopped fresh thyme OR 1/2 tsp dried

1/2 tsp chili powder

1/2 tsp black pepper

8 jumbo shrimp, peeled and deveined

12 jumbo scallops

In a large sauté pan, heat the tomato juice; sauté the onion, celery and green pepper about 2 minutes or until tender. Toss in the garlic and sauté another 1 minute. Add the tomatoes, basil, thyme, chili powder and black pepper. Bring to a boil and reduce to a simmer. Add the shrimp and scallops and poach about 4 minutes or until scallops turn white and shrimp are pink. Do not overcook. Serve with a flavoured rice.

Wear light-coloured clothing while working out on hot sunny days.

Substitution:
• Substitute 1-inch-thick swordfish for the scallops.

Option:
• Add 2 tbsp dry red wine with the tomatoes.

Scallops with Tomatoes and Zucchini

SERVES 4

CALORIES PER SERVING: 173.0

FAT (G) PER SERVING: 4.7

Scallops are a very flavourful but low-fat seafood.

1 tbsp canola oil

1 medium red onion, chopped

1 medium zucchini, cubed

1 small green pepper, chopped

1/2 cup vegetable stock (low-sodium/low-fat)

2 large tomatoes, chopped

24 large scallops

1/4 cup chopped fresh dill

1/2 tsp black pepper

In a large, deep sauté pan, heat the oil. Gently sauté the onion, zucchini and green pepper 4 minutes or until tender. Add the stock, tomatoes and scallops. Cook for 5 minutes, turning occasionally. Add the dill and black pepper and cook for another 2 minutes or until scallops have turned white.

Exercise can help to improve your sense of well-being, personal value and self-esteem.

Substitution:
- *Substitute 6 cups button mushrooms for the scallops.*

Seafood Grill with Lemons and Herbs

SERVES 4

CALORIES PER SERVING: 142.1

FAT (G) PER SERVING: 1.8

A seafood grill is a quick and easy dinner all year round. This recipe allows you the freedom to use the seafood you like the most. (Swordfish and shrimp are considered extra-lean seafood.)

4 12-inch wooden skewers
1 tbsp lemon zest
Juice of 1 lemon
1 cup dry white wine OR apple juice
1/2 cup chopped fresh mint
2 tbsp chopped fresh tarragon
1/2 tsp black pepper
1 8-oz swordfish steak, cut into 1-inch cubes

8 jumbo shrimp, peeled and deveined
1 medium zucchini, cut into rounds
1 medium red onion, cut into large chunks
1 large red pepper, cut into large chunks
1 lemon, sliced
1/2 cup chopped fresh parsley

Soak the skewers in water for 20 minutes. In a deep casserole dish, combine the lemon zest, lemon juice, wine or apple juice, mint, tarragon and black pepper. Add the swordfish and shrimp; marinate at least 1 hour. On the skewers, alternate the swordfish, zucchini, shrimp, onion and red pepper; make sure each skewer has 2 shrimp. Grill about 2 minutes each side or until the swordfish turns white, the shrimp turn pink and the vegetables have grill marks. Remove to platter and garnish with lemon slices and parsley.

Weight-lifting helps to boost your metabolism by burning calories even when your body is at rest, increases energy, and makes for quick and efficient weight loss.

Minty Seafood Rice Medley

SERVES 10

CALORIES PER SERVING: 331.2

FAT (G) PER SERVING: 2.0

I absolutely love any rice dish. This easy-to-prepare dish makes it convenient for you to enjoy quality time with your family or friends.

6 cups vegetable stock (low-sodium/low-fat)

1 19-oz can stewed tomatoes, chopped

1/2 tsp dried oregano

1/2 tsp dried tarragon

1/2 tsp black pepper

3 cups rice

1 medium onion, chopped

1 fennel bulb, chopped

1 red pepper, chopped

1/2 cup frozen corn

3 medium carrots, finely chopped or grated

1/2 cup frozen peas

12 medium shrimp, peeled and deveined

2 cups medium scallops

1 cup canned red clams, drained and rinsed

1 swordfish OR tuna steak, cubed

1/2 cup fresh mint, chopped

In a large oven-proof pot, combine the stock, tomatoes, oregano, tarragon and black pepper. Bring to a boil. Add the rice, onion, fennel, red pepper, corn, carrots and peas. Bake in a preheated oven at 350°F for 10 minutes. Mix in the seafood and mint. Bake for another 10 minutes or until rice and seafood are cooked.

Well-toned upper arms not only look good, they're also stronger, making everyday jobs such as carrying the shopping and raking the yard all the more easier.

Ken's Favourite Fish Stew

SERVES 6

CALORIES PER SERVING: 221.7

FAT (G) PER SERVING: 3.7

Growing up many years ago (I won't tell you how many) on the prairies, I rarely had an opportunity to sample seafood. Today, with the abundance and choice at my local supermarket, I'm in my glory.

1 28-oz can stewed tomatoes
2 celery stalks, chopped
2 carrots, chopped
1 medium red onion, cut into rings
1 red pepper, sliced
1 small zucchini, cubed
4 cups fish stock (low-sodium/low-fat)
1 cup tomato juice
1/4 cup chopped fresh basil
1/4 cup chopped fresh dill
2 cloves garlic, chopped

1/2 tsp chili powder
1/2 tsp black pepper
1 bay leaf
1 small swordfish steak, cut into 1-inch cubes
1 small tuna steak, cut into 1-inch cubes
12 medium shrimp, peeled and deveined
1 cup squid cut into rings or pieces
1 can clams, drained and rinsed
2 tbsp chopped fresh parsley

In a large soup pot, combine the tomatoes, celery, carrots, onion, red pepper, zucchini, stock, tomato juice, basil, dill, garlic, chili powder, black pepper and bay leaf. Simmer on medium heat, 20 minutes or until the liquid has reduced by half. Add the seafood and cook another 5 to 6 minutes. Be careful not to overcook the seafood. Remove bay leaf. Serve hot, sprinkled with parsley.

Substitutions:
- Use any other seafood or add more.
- Replace the squid with 1 cup scallops.

Poached Swordfish in Tomatoes and Basil

SERVES 4

CALORIES PER SERVING: 235.7

FAT (G) PER SERVING: 5.0

Swordfish is one of my favourite catches from the sea. The fish is very rich, so a smaller portion is recommended. Swordfish is considered an extra-lean seafood.

1 28-oz can stewed tomatoes	2 tbsp capers
1/2 cup tomato juice	2 tbsp chopped fresh parsley
1/2 cup dry red wine	1/2 tsp black pepper
1 red pepper, chopped	1/2 tsp chili powder
1/2 cup chopped fresh basil OR	1 bay leaf
1 tbsp dried	2 8-oz swordfish steaks,
1 medium onion, chopped	cut into 2

In a large frying pan or sauté pan, combine the tomatoes, tomato juice, wine, pepper, basil, onion, capers, parsley, black pepper, chili powder and bay leaf. Bring to a boil and reduce to a simmer. Add the swordfish and poach for 4 minutes. Gently turn fish and continue poaching another 4 minutes or until the swordfish has turned white. Do not overcook this fish, as even with poaching it could become dry. Remove bay leaf. Transfer fish to plates and serve immediately with the tomato-basil sauce over top.

If exercising in the heat is completely new to you, take it easy for the first two weeks.

Substitution:
• Replace swordfish with tuna steaks.

Poached Swordfish with Tomatoes and Pears

SERVES 4

CALORIES PER SERVING: 186.5

FAT (G) PER SERVING: 3.0

Swordfish is available in most supermarkets fresh or frozen. This fish has a very meaty texture and is perfect for poaching. Swordfish usually comes in steak sizes and can be cut into 2 because it also is a very rich fish.

1 19-oz can low-sodium stewed tomatoes	1/4 cup chopped fresh basil OR 1/2 tsp dried
1 medium onion, chopped	1 tsp paprika
2 cloves garlic, chopped	1/2 tsp black pepper
2 pears, cored and chopped	1 bay leaf
1/2 cup unsweetened pear nectar or juice	2 swordfish steaks, cut into 2 OR 4 small steaks
	1/2 cup chopped fresh parsley

In a large sauté pan, combine the tomatoes, onion, garlic, pears, pear juice, basil, paprika, pepper and bay leaf. Bring to a boil; reduce to a simmer. Add the swordfish and cover with the liquid. Simmer, covered, 8 to 10 minutes, turning once. Add the parsley or the last 2 minutes. The swordfish should be completely white and still moist when cooked. Remove bay leaf. Place the fish on plates and spoon over the poaching mixture.

Substitutions:
• Replace the swordfish with tuna steaks.
• Replace the pears and nectar with 2 cups seedless grapes and 1/2 cup unsweetened white grape juice.

Swordfish with Pineapple Sauce

SERVES 4

CALORIES PER SERVING: 132.6

FAT (G) PER SERVING: 2.7

Swordfish is one of my favourites, particularly when it's served with a fruit-based relish or sauce.

2 tbsp lemon juice	1 red pepper, chopped
2 12-oz swordfish steaks, cut into 2	1 small red onion, finely chopped
1 tsp dried tarragon	2 cloves garlic, chopped
1 tsp black pepper	1 tsp white wine vinegar
1 cup chopped pineapple	1/4 cup fresh parsley, chopped
1/4 cup apple juice	1 tbsp chopped fresh mint OR 1/2 tsp dried

Sprinkle the lemon juice evenly on the swordfish steaks, then sprinkle with the tarragon and 1/2 tsp of the black pepper. Grill on high for 10 to 12 minutes, turning once and to obtain grill marks. Meanwhile, in a small saucepan, combine the pineapple, apple juice, red pepper, onion, garlic, vinegar, parsley, mint and remaining black pepper. Simmer about 8 minutes and serve on top of swordfish.

Exercise can help provide you with the extra energy you need to maintain your sanity during cold-weather months. The endorphin highs you get from exercising can hold you over until the weather warms up.

Substitution:
• Substitute grilled chicken for the swordfish.

Roasted Tuna with Red Peppers and Fennel

SERVES 4

CALORIES PER SERVING: 310.1

FAT (G) PER SERVING: 8.8

Forget canned tuna! Buy it fresh and roast, grill or poach it.

1/2 cup vegetable stock (low-sodium/low-fat)

1/2 tsp dried mint

1/2 tsp dried thyme

1/2 cup fresh parsley, chopped

2 12-oz tuna steaks, cut into 2

2 tbsp lemon juice

1/2 tsp chili powder

1/2 tsp black pepper

2 red peppers, sliced

1 medium red onion, sliced

2 cloves garlic, chopped

1 fennel bulb, sliced

In a large, deep baking dish, combine the stock, mint, thyme and parsley. Place the tuna in the baking dish. Sprinkle with the lemon juice, chili powder and black pepper. Place the red peppers, onion, garlic and fennel on top and around the sides, if room permits. Roast, in a preheated oven at 350°F for 20 minutes, turning once, until the tuna is moist. Serve fish with the red pepper, fennel and onion on top.

Incorporate strength training into your workouts to increase your bone density.

Substitution:
• Substitute chicken or turkey for the tuna; roast for at least 30 minutes.

Stuffed Sole with Mushrooms and Sweet Red Pepper Relish

SERVES 4

CALORIES PER SERVING: 187.8

FAT (G) PER SERVING: 2.5

This relish offers a new way to serve up an old favourite.

1 cup button mushrooms, chopped

2 carrots, julienned

1/4 cup chopped fresh basil OR 1/2 tsp dried

1/2 tsp dried thyme

4 large sole fillets

1 bunch green onions, julienned

1 cup vegetable stock (low-sodium/low-fat)

1 red pepper, chopped

1/4 cup chopped fresh mint OR 1/2 tsp dried

1/4 tsp liquid sweetener such as Equal

Pinch black pepper

In a non-stick sauté pan, or a pan sprayed with cooking spray, gently sauté the mushrooms and carrots about 4 minutes. Remove from heat and stir in the basil and thyme. Lay the sole flat and evenly distribute the cooked vegetables and the green onions over the fish. Roll up sole lengthwise and place in a baking dish. Evenly distribute 1/2 cup of the stock over the fish. Bake in a preheated oven at 350°F 8 to 10 minutes.

Meanwhile, to prepare the relish in a food processor combine the remaining stock, red pepper, mint and sweetener. Purée until smooth. Place in small saucepan and heat on medium heat about 5 minutes. Serve warm on top of the fish. Garnish fish and relish with freshly ground black pepper.

Substitutions:
• Replace sole with orange roughy or turbot.
• Replace button mushrooms with more flavourful Portobello, shiitake or porcini.

POULTRY

Baked Chicken with Grapefruit and Tarragon

SERVES 4

CALORIES PER SERVING: 211.9

FAT (G) PER SERVING: 5.7

Adding fruit, especially citrus, to main meals makes a different but healthful and flavourful meal.

2 medium grapefruits

1 tbsp canola oil

4 skinless chicken breasts, bone in

1/2 cup chicken stock (low-sodium/low-fat)

1/2 cup chopped fresh tarragon

1 bunch green onions, chopped

1 tsp black pepper

Remove zest from 1 grapefruit and juice the grapefruit. Slice remaining grapefruit. Set aside. In an oven-proof sauté pan, heat the oil and gently brown the chicken for about 8 minutes on each side. Remove from pan. In the pan, place the grapefruit slices; add the stock and 1/4 cup of the tarragon. Return the chicken to the pan and add the grapefruit juice, remaining tarragon, onions, black pepper and 1 tbsp of the grapefruit zest. If there are some grapefruit slices left, place on top of the chicken. Bake in a preheated oven at 350°F for 25 minutes or until chicken is cooked through.

Substitutions:
- Substitute 3 medium oranges for the grapefruit.
- Substitute fresh mint or parsley for the tarragon.

Garlic-Roasted Chicken and Fennel with Rosemary and Thyme

SERVES 4

CALORIES PER SERVING: 251

FAT (G) PER SERVING: 2

The Italians refer to this recipe as everyday fare and nothing special. Every time I prepare it for company they think it is special, especially the aroma.

4 skinless chicken breasts, bone in	2 medium carrots, sliced
1 red onion, chopped	1/4 cup finely chopped fresh rosemary OR 1/2 tsp dried
3 medium potatoes, cubed	1 tbsp finely chopped fresh thyme OR 1/2 tsp dried
12 cloves garlic	
1 medium fennel bulb, sliced	2 small tomatoes, chopped

In a non-stick pan, or a sauté pan sprayed with cooking spray, over medium heat, brown the chicken 10 minutes on each side. Remove the chicken to a deep baking dish. In the pan, gently sauté the onion for about 3 minutes; add the potatoes and garlic cloves; brown another 3 minutes. Transfer to the baking dish and add the fennel, carrots, rosemary and thyme. Roast, covered, in a preheated oven at 350°F for 15 minutes. Uncover and add tomatoes. Broil for 5 minutes.

Feeling dizzy or faint while exercising? Rest and drink water until you recover.

Substitution:
• *Replace the chicken with turkey.*

Grilled Lemon Chicken with Rosemary

SERVES 4

CALORIES PER SERVING: 151 3

FAT (G) PER SERVING: 1.7

In Tuscany this dish is prepared with chicken and rabbit. I serve this recipe all year round using an indoor grill.

4 skinless chicken breasts, bone in	1 tbsp garlic powder
	1 tbsp onion powder
4 lemons	1 tsp black pepper
1/4 cup finely chopped fresh rosemary OR 4 tsp dried	1/2 tsp paprika

Coat the chicken with the juice of 2 lemons. Combine the rosemary, garlic powder, onion powder, black pepper and paprika. Sprinkle three-quarters of the mixture evenly over the chicken, cover and refrigerate for at least 3 hours or overnight. Grill on high for about 20 minutes, turning chicken for the last 5 minutes. Slice the remaining 2 lemons and grill last 5 minutes with chicken to use as garnish.

Substitutions:
- Substitute turkey for the chicken.
- Substitute limes for lemons.

Herb Chicken with Roasted Almonds

SERVES 4

CALORIES PER SERVING: 286.0

FAT (G) PER SERVING: 14.5

The almond, which hails from the Mediterranean, is high in fat. In this dish, however, almonds are used sparingly.

4 skinless chicken breasts, bone in	1/4 cup chopped fresh basil OR 1/2 tsp dried
1/2 tsp black pepper	1 tbsp chopped fresh sage OR 1/2 tsp dried
1/2 tsp celery seed (optional)	1 tbsp chopped fresh oregano OR 1/2 tsp dried
1 tbsp canola oil	1/2 cup sliced almonds
2 tbsp minced garlic	
1 medium red onion, sliced	

Sprinkle the chicken with the black pepper and celery seed (if using). In a sauté pan, heat the oil. Brown the chicken about 10 minutes, turning once. Remove. Coat the chicken with the garlic. In a deep non-stick baking dish, place onion and chicken. Combine the basil, sage and oregano. Sprinkle half of the mixture over the chicken. Cover and bake in a preheated oven at 350°F for 20 minutes. Remove cover and sprinkle with remaining herb mixture and almonds. Return to oven another 5 minutes or until almonds are toasted.

Consider hiring a personal trainer to map out a regimen and help you set goals.

Sweet Red Peppers and Chicken

SERVES 4

CALORIES PER SERVING: 111.9

FAT (G) PER SERVING: 1.1

Red peppers are available year round and easy to find. I use red peppers not only for their sweet tangy flavour but also for the colour they add.

2 boned, skinless chicken breasts, sliced	2 sweet red peppers, sliced
1 medium red onion, sliced	1 cup chicken stock (low-sodium/low-fat)
2 cloves garlic, chopped	1/2 cup chopped fresh parsley
2 celery stalks, julienned	

In a non-stick sauté pan, or a pan coated with cooking spray, sauté the chicken for 8 to 10 minutes or until meat is no longer pink. Add the onion and garlic; sauté another 2 to 3 minutes or until the onion is translucent. Add the celery, red peppers and stock. Mix well and bring to boil; reduce to medium heat. Sauté for 5 minutes. Add the parsley. Cook another 2 minutes or until stock has reduced by half. Serve with rice.

The flabbiness that appears at the back of the upper arms is caused by too much fat and not enough muscle. Fat-burning and muscle-toning exercises will help get rid of those "bat wings."

Red Pepper–Stuffed Chicken

SERVES 4

CALORIES PER SERVING: 289.1

FAT (G) PER SERVING: 7.3

Prepare this dish in advance to spend more time with your family and friends.

4 medium red peppers

3/4 cup apple juice

3 tbsp chopped fresh tarragon OR

1 tsp dried

4 medium boned, skinless chicken breasts, pounded thin

1/2 tsp dried basil

1/2 tsp black pepper

1 cup chopped fresh parsley

1/2 cup shredded low-fat mozzarella cheese

Chop 1 red pepper. In a blender, combine chopped pepper with apple juice and half of the tarragon. Purée until smooth. Chill. Thinly slice remaining red peppers and distribute evenly over the chicken breasts. Sprinkle with remaining tarragon, the basil, black pepper, parsley and cheese. Roll up chicken breasts and secure with a toothpick. Place in a non-stick baking pan. Bake in a preheated oven at 350°F for 25 minutes. Serve chilled sauce over the chicken.

Avoid exercising outdoors when the air pollution index is high.

Stuffed Chicken Breasts

SERVES 4

CALORIES PER SERVING: 253.5

FAT (G) PER SERVING: 7.7

This stuffed chicken recipe is a low-fat version of Chicken Spinach Roll-Ups, which appeared in my first cookbook.

2 cups spinach, finely chopped	1/2 tsp dried basil
1 cup mushrooms, chopped	1/2 tsp dried oregano
1 small red pepper, chopped	1/2 tsp black pepper
2 cloves garlic, chopped	1/2 cup shredded low-fat
2 tbsp Dijon mustard	mozzarella cheese
2 tbsp non-fat sour cream	4 boned, skinless chicken breasts,
1 tsp chili powder	pounded thin

In a medium mixing bowl, combine the spinach, mushrooms, red pepper, garlic, mustard, sour cream, 1/2 tsp of the chili powder, the basil, oregano, black pepper and cheese. Mix together and spread on top of the chicken. Roll up chicken and secure with a toothpick. Place chicken in a non-stick baking dish and sprinkle with the remaining chili powder. Bake in a preheated oven at 350°F for 25 minutes.

> Generally, people over 50 should spend more time warming up and cooling down than younger individuals—average about 15 to 20 minutes for each.

Roasted Chicken Breasts with Apple and Cinnamon

SERVES 4

CALORIES PER SERVING: 422.7

FAT (G) PER SERVING: 9.1

This is a real treat and very easy to prepare.

2 tbsp canola oil	1/2 cup chopped fresh parsley
4 skinless chicken breasts, bone in	2 tbsp apple juice concentrate
4 medium potatoes, quartered	4 apples, cored and quartered
1/2 cup apple juice	1 tsp cinnamon
1 medium onion, chopped	1/2 tsp black pepper
	1/4 tsp dried sage

In an oven-proof sauté pan or skillet, heat the oil. Gently brown the chicken for 10 minutes, turning once. Microwave the potatoes on high for 3 minutes; add to the sauté pan along with the apple juice, onion and parsley. Using a brush, coat the chicken with apple juice concentrate; add the apples to the dish. Evenly sprinkle the cinnamon and pepper over the chicken, apples and potatoes. Sprinkle sage on the chicken. Roast in a preheated oven at 350°F for 30 minutes or until chicken is white and cooked through.

Rehydrate often while exercising. (You are dehydrated before you feel thirsty.)

Substitution:
- *Replace the chicken with turkey.*

Roasted Chicken with Potatoes and Carrots

SERVES 4

CALORIES PER SERVING: 273.5

FAT (G) PER SERVING: 5.2

Roast chicken is a healthy and quick dinner, if prepared properly. I always remove the skin and any visible fat.

1 lemon	1/2 tsp dried sage
1 tbsp canola oil	1/2 tsp dried rosemary
4 skinless chicken breasts	1/2 tsp garlic powder
1/2 cup dry white wine	1/2 tsp onion powder
1/2 cup chicken stock (low-sodium/low-fat)	2 medium potatoes, cubed
	3 large carrots, julienned
1/2 tsp black pepper	

Remove 1 tbsp zest from lemon. Juice the lemon. Set aside zest and juice. In a sauté pan or frying pan, heat the oil on medium heat. Sauté the chicken for about 10 minutes, turning once, until just browned. Transfer chicken to a large baking dish and add the wine, stock and lemon juice. Sprinkle the chicken with pepper, sage, rosemary, garlic powder, onion powder and the lemon zest. Place the potatoes and carrots along the sides. Bake in a preheated oven at 350°F for about 25 minutes basting chicken with the liquid at least 4 times. For the last 2 minutes, broil the chicken to brown the top.

Substitution:
- *Replace the chicken breasts with 1 turkey breast cut into 2.*

Stir-Fried Chicken and Savoury Vegetables

SERVES 4

CALORIES PER SERVING: 219.4

FAT (G) PER SERVING: 1.3

The frying in this recipe is done with soup stock instead of fat and has as much flavour.

1/2 cup chicken OR vegetable stock (low-sodium/low-fat)

2 large boned, skinless chicken breasts, sliced into strips

1 large onion, sliced

2 cloves garlic, chopped

1 cup broccoli florets

1 cup green beans, cut on diagonal

2 medium carrots, thinly sliced lengthwise

1 medium red pepper, thinly sliced lengthwise

1 medium green pepper, thinly sliced lengthwise

1 cup chopped fresh parsley

1/2 tsp dried basil

1/2 tsp dried thyme

1/2 tsp black pepper

1/4 cup low-sodium soy sauce

1/4 cup liquid honey

In a wok or a large sauté pan, heat the stock and sauté the chicken for 10 minutes or until meat is no longer pink. Add the onion and garlic and sauté another 5 minutes. Add the broccoli, green beans, carrots, red pepper, green pepper, parsley, basil, thyme and black pepper. Sauté about 4 minutes. Make a hole in the centre of the mixture. Combine the soy sauce and honey and pour into the centre. Cook for 2 minutes, then mix well; sauté for another 4 to 5 minutes or until liquid has reduced by half. Serve with flavoured rice.

> Substitution:
> • Substitute thinly sliced round steak or turkey for the chicken.

Stuffed Turkey Bundles in Tomato Sauce

SERVES 4

CALORIES PER SERVING: 337.7

FAT (G) PER SERVING: 12.0

These bundles are always a crowd pleaser. The nice thing about this recipe is you can be as creative with the stuffing as you want to be.

1 large turkey breast, sliced into 4 cutlets or scaloppine
2 tbsp Dijon mustard
4 slices low-fat ham
1/2 cup shredded low-fat mozzarella cheese
1 cup chopped spinach
1 tbsp canola oil

1 28-oz can stewed tomatoes
2 cloves garlic, chopped
1/2 cup fresh basil, chopped OR 1/2 tsp dried
1/2 cup fresh parsley, chopped OR 1 tsp dried
1/2 tsp black pepper

Lay the turkey slices flat and evenly spread with the mustard. Lay 1 slice of ham on each piece and sprinkle with cheese. Evenly distribute spinach on top of the cutlets. Roll up and secure with a toothpick. Heat the oil in a large sauté pan or frying pan and brown the turkey bundles on all sides, about 4 minutes in total. Add the tomatoes, garlic, basil, parsley and black pepper. Simmer for 15 minutes and serve with rice or pasta and sauce.

Choose an activity you enjoy doing.

Substitution:
• Replace the spinach with parsley, and replace the parsley in the sauce with coriander.

Addition:
• Add 1/4 cup dry red wine with the tomatoes.

Sesame Grilled Turkey and Vegetable Kabobs

SERVES 6

CALORIES PER SERVING: 276.2

FAT (G) PER SERVING: 8.9

Grilling is one of my favourite ways to prepare a healthy dinner.

6 8-inch wooden skewers	1 green pepper, quartered
1 1/2 lb lean turkey breast, cubed	3 tbsp sesame oil
	1 tsp garlic powder
1 medium zucchini, cut into 1/2-inch slices	1 tsp paprika
	1/2 tsp dried thyme
1 large red onion, cut into thick wedges	1/2 tsp black pepper
	2 tbsp chopped fresh coriander
1 cup coarsely chopped cauliflower	OR Italian parsley
1 cup broccoli florets	1 tbsp sesame seeds

Soak skewers in water for 20 minutes. Evenly thread the turkey, zucchini, onion, cauliflower, broccoli and green pepper on the skewers. Gently brush the turkey and vegetables with sesame oil. Combine garlic powder, paprika, thyme and black pepper. Sprinkle over the kabobs. Grill kabobs for 18 to 20 minutes, turning 4 times to achieve grill marks. For the last 5 minutes, sprinkle on the coriander and sesame seeds. Serve immediately.

> When exercising in the heat, a person of average weight should drink at least 12 cups of water a day. An overweight individual needs even more. Children should drink about 6 to 8 cups of water a day.

Baked Turkey with Pineapple Salsa

SERVES 4

CALORIES PER SERVING: 285.5

FAT (G) PER SERVING: 9.6

Turkey is one of my favourite low-fat options. Today you can purchase turkey steaks, or a half breast, which, when halved, again makes a great steak.

1 cup diced pineapple (see note)	2 tbsp unsweetened shredded coconut
1 small red onion, chopped	4 medium turkey steaks
1 small red pepper, chopped	1/2 cup unsweetened pineapple juice
2 tbsp chopped fresh tarragon OR	1/2 tsp garlic powder
1 tsp dried	1/2 tsp black pepper

To prepare the salsa, in a small mixing bowl, combine pineapple, onion, red pepper, 1 tbsp of the tarragon and 2 tbsp coconut. Mix well and chill. In a baking dish, place the turkey and pour the pineapple juice on top. Sprinkle with the garlic powder, black pepper and remaining tarragon. Bake in preheated oven at 350°F for 20 minutes. Broil for 5 minutes more, until golden. Serve with the pineapple salsa on top.

Note: If you use canned, be sure it is unsweetened.

If you are not sure about your level of exercise, check with your physician first.

Substitution:
- *Replace turkey with chicken breasts.*

Turkey Steak with Apple Relish

SERVES 4

CALORIES PER SERVING: 216.0

FAT (G) PER SERVING: 4.1

A 4-oz boned turkey cutlet without the skin and fat has less then 1 gram of fat!

1/2 cup vegetable stock (low-sodium/low-fat)
1/2 cup apple juice
4 4-oz boned turkey cutlets
3 apples, cored and cubed

1 1/2 tbsp chopped fresh basil, OR 1/4 tsp dried
1/4 tsp cinnamon
2 tbsp chopped fresh parsley

In a non-stick frying pan over medium heat, heat 1/4 cup of the vegetable stock and 1/4 cup of the apple juice. Add the turkey cutlets and cook about 2 minutes on each side. Add apples, basil, cinnamon and parsley; cook another 10 minutes, until the liquid has reduced, producing an apple relish. Serve the relish on top of the turkey or on the side.

Substitutions:
- *Substitute pears for the apples.*
- *Substitute oregano for the basil.*
- *Substitute 1 tbsp chopped fresh mint for the parsley.*

Grilled Cornish Game Hen with Sesame and Rosemary

SERVES 4

CALORIES PER SERVING: 181.0

FAT (G) PER SERVING: 8.0

Cornish game hens are a real treat and perfect for a dinner party.

1/2 cup chicken stock (low-sodium/low-fat)	1/2 tsp chili powder
1 tbsp sesame oil	1/2 tsp black pepper
2 tbsp chopped fresh rosemary	2 large skinless Cornish game hens
1/2 tsp onion powder	(2 lb each), cut in half
1/2 tsp garlic powder	1/2 cup fresh parsley, chopped
	1 tsp sesame seeds

In a small mixing bowl, combine the stock, sesame oil, 1 tbsp of the rosemary, the onion powder, garlic powder, chili powder and pepper. Brush the Cornish hen halves with the mixture and refrigerate for about 30 minutes hour. When ready to grill, set grill on high and place the hens skin down to get grill marks; turn after 5 minutes. Grill for 15 minutes, basting occasionally with the sauce. Sprinkle with the remaining rosemary and the sesame seeds. Continue to grill another 10 minutes or until no pink is showing under the wing. Garnish hens with fresh parsley.

MEAT

Lamb Stew with Lemon and Fennel

SERVES 6

CALORIES PER SERVING: 312.7

FAT (G) PER SERVING: 9.6

The combination of lamb and fennel works well because both have a strong, distinct flavour. The roasted vegetables add great texture to this stew.

1 tbsp canola oil	4 cups beef stock (low-sodium/low-fat)
2 lb lean stewing lamb, cubed	1/4 cup dry white wine
1 fennel bulb, chopped	1 tbsp lemon zest
1 red pepper, chopped	Juice of 2 lemons
2 carrots, julienned	1 tsp dried basil
2 medium potatoes, cubed	1 tsp dried mint
1 small zucchini, chopped	1/4 cup fresh parsley, chopped
1 medium red onion, chopped	
1 tsp dried oregano	

In a large soup pot on medium heat, heat the oil. Brown the lamb in batches for about 5 minutes. While you are browning the meat, place the fennel, red pepper, carrots, potatoes, zucchini and red onion on a cookie sheet, spray with cooking spray. Sprinkle the vegetables with the oregano. Broil in the oven or grill on an indoor grill until golden. To the lamb add the stock, wine, lemon zest, lemon juice, basil and mint. Simmer for 5 minutes. Add the roasted vegetables. Simmer another 10 minutes or until the liquid has reduced by about a third. Just before serving, stir in parsley.

Substitution:
• Replace the lamb with 4 boned, skinless chicken breasts cut into chunks.

Mediterranean Lamb Stew

SERVES 6

CALORIES PER SERVING: 301.1

FAT (G) PER SERVING: 8.2

This lamb stew calls for vegetables and herbs from the Mediterranean.

1 tsp canola oil
1 1/2 lb lean stewing lamb, cut into 1-inch cubes
1/2 cup dried apricots, cranberries OR apples
1 medium onion, chopped
2 cloves garlic, chopped
2 carrots, chopped
1 red pepper, chopped
2 tomatoes, chopped
2 medium potatoes, cubed
1 apple, cored and chopped

1 small turnip, cubed (about 1 cup)
4 cups beef stock (low-sodium/low-fat)
1/2 cup dry red wine
1/2 cup apple juice
1/2 tsp cinnamon
1/2 tsp dried basil
1/2 tsp dried rosemary
1/2 tsp dried mint
1/2 tsp black pepper
1 bay leaf

In a large soup pot or crock pot, heat the oil. Gently brown the lamb in batches for about 5 minutes. Add the dried apricots, onion, garlic, carrots, red pepper, tomatoes, potatoes, apple, turnip, stock, wine, apple juice, cinnamon, basil, rosemary, mint, black pepper and bay leaf. Bring to a boil; reduce heat and simmer for 20 minutes or until liquid has reduced by half. Remove bay leaf.

As you age, gaining a few pounds may be considered normal, but it's not inevitable—exercise can help you get rid of "spare tires."

Substitution:
• Substitute lean beef or chicken pieces for the lamb.

Orange and Garlic Lamb Chops

SERVES 4

CALORIES PER SERVING: 189.7

FAT (G) PER SERVING: 8.1

Orange and mint is a great combination with lamb.

4 lamb chops, 3/4-inch thick, trimmed of fat	1 tsp canola oil
2 tbsp orange zest	Juice of orange, with pulp
1/2 tsp black pepper	1 clove garlic, chopped
	1/2 tsp dried mint

Sprinkle both sides of lamb with 1 tbsp of the orange zest and the pepper. In a frying pan, heat the oil over high heat. Sear lamb about 3 minutes on each side for medium, longer for well done. Remove the lamb chops and keep warm. Add the orange juice, remaining zest, the garlic and mint. Deglaze the pan, stirring to scrape up brown bits, and reduce the sauce by half. Serve sauce over the lamb chops.

It is never too late to start exercizing, which can slow down the aging process.

Substitution:
• Replace lamb chops with chicken breasts.

Poached Veal in Cranberry and Red Wine Sauce

SERVES 4

CALORIES PER SERVING: 286.5

FAT (G) PER SERVING: 6.0

I had a version of this recipe in Milan prepared by my friend Alberto's wife. Cranberries add real flavour to this veal dish.

1 cup unsweetened cranberry juice	1/2 tsp dried oregano
1/4 cup red wine	1/2 tsp black pepper
1 small red onion, finely chopped	4 large thin veal cutlets
1 clove garlic, finely chopped	1/2 cup frozen cranberries OR fresh
1/2 tsp dried rosemary	1/2 cup chopped fresh parsley

In a deep sauté pan, combine the cranberry juice, wine, onion, garlic, rosemary, oregano and pepper; bring to a boil. Reduce to a simmer and add the veal. Poach about 10 minutes. Add the cranberries and parsley. Cook another 5 minutes or until the veal is cooked through.

If you are exercising and cannot carry-on a light conversation, slow down.

Substitution:
• Replace veal with chicken breasts and poach at least 10 minutes longer.

Veal Stuffed with Ricotta and Parsley

SERVES 4

CALORIES PER SERVING: 200.7

FAT (G) PER SERVING: 4.4

This is one of my favourite quick recipes for company.

1 small red onion, cut in chunks	1/4 tsp dried thyme
1 small red pepper, cut in chunks	1/4 tsp dried mint
1 clove garlic	1/2 tsp black pepper
1 cup fresh parsley	4 large thin veal cutlets
1/2 cup low-fat ricotta cheese	1/2 tsp paprika

In a food processor or blender, finely chop the onion, red pepper, garlic and parsley; add the ricotta, thyme, mint and black pepper. Blend until smooth. Spread the stuffing over the veal. Roll up the veal and secure with a toothpick. Place in a non-stick baking dish. Sprinkle with the paprika. Bake in a preheated oven at 350°F for 20 minutes. Serve immediately.

Go swimming with your children.

Substitution:
* *Replace the veal with thinly pounded boned, skinless chicken breasts.*

Pork Chops with Lemon and Sage

SERVES 4

CALORIES PER SERVING: 183.3

FAT (G) PER SERVING: 10.5

I love the robust flavour of this other white meat.

4 medium pork chops	2 tbsp chopped fresh sage
1 tbsp canola oil	Juice of 1 lemon
1 tbsp calorie-reduced margarine	1/2 tsp black pepper

Trim all visible fat from the pork chops. In a non-stick frying pan, heat the oil and margarine. Add the sage and stir for 30 seconds. Add the pork chops and sauté about 3 to 4 minutes each side. Add the lemon juice and pepper and sauté for another 2 minutes or until meat is cooked through. Serve immediately.

Exercising outdoors on crisp, cool, blue-sky days can be spiritually uplifting.

Substitution:
• Replace the canola oil with olive oil.

Roast Pork Chops with Potato and Orange

SERVES 4

CALORIES PER SERVING: 277.4

FAT (G) PER SERVING: 9.3

When I was growing up, a dinner of pork chops with apples and applesauce was something the whole family looked forward to. This variation calls for oranges and orange juice.

1 tbsp canola oil	3 cloves garlic, chopped
4 medium pork chops, trimmed of fat	1/2 tsp dried tarragon
1 medium orange, sliced	1/2 tsp dried mint
3 medium potatoes, cubed	1/2 tsp black pepper
1 red pepper, sliced	1 tbsp orange zest

In an oven-proof frying pan, heat the oil and gently brown both sides of the pork chops. Remove chops and drain any oil or fat from pan. Place the orange slices in the pan and top with the pork chops. Surround the chops with the potatoes and red pepper. Sprinkle with the garlic, tarragon, mint and black pepper. Roast in a pre-heated oven at 350°F for 20 minutes. Add the orange zest and roast another 5 minutes or until the pork chops are cooked right through and potatoes are tender.

> Work your larger muscles first and the smaller ones last.

Pork Loin Chops with Orange, Mint and Red Pepper

SERVES 4

CALORIES PER SERVING: 270.2

FAT (G) PER SERVING: 12.7

Pork is the other white meat that sometimes gets a bad rap. I trim all extra fat even though today's pork is very lean.

2 tbsp canola oil
4 boneless pork loin chops, trimmed of fat
1 medium red onion, chopped
1 medium orange, thinly sliced
1 red pepper, chopped
Juice of one medium orange
2 tbsp orange juice concentrate

1/2 tsp black pepper
1/4 tsp dried basil
1/2 cup mint, chopped
1/2 cup parsley, chopped
1/4 cup beef stock (low-sodium/low-fat)
1 tbsp orange zest

In a deep sauté pan, heat the oil. Brown the pork chops for about 15 minutes; remove. Add the onion, orange slices and red pepper. Sauté about 3 minutes. Add the orange juice, orange juice concentrate, black pepper, basil, mint and parsley; mix well. Add the chops and simmer about 10 minutes or until liquid has reduced by half and pork is cooked through. Stir in the orange zest and serve immediately.

Substitution:
• Substitute boned chicken breasts or turkey cutlets for the pork chops.

Pork Tenderloins with a Bouquet of Herbs and Garlic

SERVES 4

CALORIES PER SERVING: 155.2

FAT (G) PER SERVING: 2.9

When preparing the herb bouquets for this recipe, don't worry about measuring the fresh herbs or not having all the specified herbs. Use what you have or what you can find.

2 1/2-lb pork tenderloins
4 cloves garlic, finely chopped
1 medium onion, sliced
6 sprigs fresh rosemary OR
3/4 tsp dried
6 sprigs fresh thyme OR
3/4 tsp dried

10 fresh basil leaves
OR 3/4 tsp dried
1/2 stems fresh oregano
OR 3/4 tsp dried
1/2 tsp black pepper
1/4 cup fresh parsley, chopped

Place tenderloins on foil wrap and evenly coat with garlic. Surround the tenderloins with the onion. Make 2 bouquets of fresh herbs by securing rosemary, thyme, basil, oregano and black pepper with string. Top each tenderloin with a bouquet. (If using dried herbs, mix together and sprinkle over evenly.) Pour 2 tbsp water onto foil to create moisture. Wrap the foil securely, transfer to a baking sheet and bake in a preheated oven at 400°F for 30 minutes or until cooked through and meat is white. Remove the bouquet and garnish with fresh parsley or fresh herbs.

Burn 13% more calories per day by doing vigorous strength training sessions.

Stir-Fried Beef with Ginger and Broccoli

SERVES 6

CALORIES PER SERVING: 150.5

FAT (G) PER SERVING: 4.4

This is one of my standards because it's quick and easy to prepare.

1/2 cup beef stock (low-sodium/low-fat)

1 lb round steak, thinly sliced

1 medium red onion, cut into wedges

2 cloves garlic, chopped

2 carrots, thinly sliced

1/2 tsp minced fresh ginger

1/4 cup low-sodium soy sauce

2 cups broccoli florets

2 tbsp chopped fresh coriander OR fresh parsley

In a frying pan or wok, heat the stock. Add the beef and stir-fry about 3 minutes. Add the onion, garlic, carrots and ginger; cook another 2 minutes. Add the soy sauce, broccoli and coriander; stir-fry another 4 minutes. Serve immediately.

Walk or cycle to the corner store instead of driving.

Substitution:
• Replace beef with jumbo shrimp.

Tomato Beef Stew

SERVES 6

CALORIES PER SERVING: 286.6

FAT (G) PER SERVING: 3.7

Stew is one of my favourite fall and winter meals. When choosing stewing beef, select very lean meat and trim any excess fat.

2 lb lean stewing beef, cubed	1 tbsp balsamic vinegar
1 28-oz can stewed tomatoes	2 cups beef stock (low-sodium/low-fat)
2 cloves garlic, chopped	
1 bunch green onions, chopped	1 tsp chili powder
2 medium potatoes, cubed	1/2 tsp dried basil
1 small zucchini, cubed	1/2 tsp dried oregano
2 medium carrots, chopped	1/2 tsp black pepper
1/2 cup dry red wine	

In a large, non-stick soup pot, brown the beef cubes in batches for about 8 to 10 minutes, turning occasionally. Add the tomatoes, garlic, half of the green onions, the potatoes, zucchini, carrots, wine, balsamic vinegar, stock, chili powder, basil, oregano and pepper. Simmer on low heat for 25 minutes or until the liquid thickens. Use remaining green onions for garnish.

Always exhale through your mouth as you lift heavy objects.

Substitution:
- *Substitute veal cubes for the beef.*

Vegetarian Substitution:
- *Substitute 2 blocks of cubed tofu for the beef. Use vegetable stock and simmer for only about 15 minutes.*

Beef Stew with Mushrooms and Herbs

SERVES 6

CALORIES PER SERVING: 192.3

FAT (G) PER SERVING: 4.2

Meat lovers will flip over this wonderful Italian beef stew. The combination of beef, mushrooms and herbs will set your taste buds on fire.

1 tbsp canola oil

1 1/2-lb lean stewing beef, cubed

All-purpose flour to dredge beef

1 medium red onion, chopped

2 medium potatoes, cubed

1 clove garlic, chopped

2 celery stalks, chopped

1 cup chopped Portobello mushrooms

1 cup button mushrooms, chopped

1/4 cup chopped fresh basil OR 1/2 tsp dried

1/4 cup chopped fresh oregano OR 1/2 tsp dried

1 tbsp chopped fresh thyme OR 1/2 tsp dried

1 tsp balsamic vinegar

1 bay leaf

1/2 tsp black pepper

2 cups beef stock (low-sodium/low-fat)

1/2 cup dry red wine

In a large soup pot, heat 1 1/2 tsp of the oil over medium heat. Dredge the beef in the flour, shaking it to remove excess. Brown the beef in batches for about 10 minutes; remove. Add remaining oil and sauté the onion, potatoes, garlic and celery 2 minutes or until onion is translucent. Add the mushrooms and continue to sauté 4 to 5 minutes. Add basil, oregano, thyme, balsamic vinegar, bay leaf, pepper, stock and wine; bring to a boil. Reduce heat, cover and simmer about 20 minutes. Remove bay leaf.

Substitution:
• Replace stewing beef with stewing veal. Omit red wine if you want.

Garlic Beef Tenderloin

SERVES 4

CALORIES PER SERVING: 281

FAT (G) PER SERVING: 12.2

Beef tenderloin is something I serve on special occasions. My neighbour Gill does a version of this that leaves us fighting for the leftovers, if there are any leftovers.

1 1/2 lb lean beef tenderloin	2 tbsp Worcestershire sauce
6 cloves garlic, cut in half	1/4 tsp dried rosemary
1/4 cup beef stock (low-sodium/low-fat)	1/4 tsp dried basil
1/4 cup low-sodium soy sauce	1/2 tsp black pepper

Cut 12 little slits all over the beef tenderloin and push garlic pieces into slits. Place the beef on a large piece of foil wrap in a baking pan. Fold the foil upwards but do not seal. Combine the stock, soy sauce, Worcestershire sauce, rosemary, basil and pepper. Pour the liquid over the beef and seal the foil, allowing some space between beef and foil. Bake in preheated oven at 400°F for 35 minutes or until desired doneness. Let sit for 10 minutes before slicing. Place beef slices on a platter and top with the juices in the foil.

Walk up the stairs instead of taking the elevator or escalator.

Beef Steak with Rosemary and Red Wine Onion Relish

SERVES 4

CALORIES PER SERVING: 331

FAT (G) PER SERVING: 13.1

Beef is an important part of the Mediterranean diet. This recipe reflects the flavours of that region.

4 6-oz New York steaks	2 cloves garlic, chopped
1/2 tsp salt	1/2 cup beef stock (low-sodium/low-fat)
1 tsp black pepper	
2 tbsp chopped fresh rosemary	1/4 cup dry red wine
1 tbsp canola oil	1/4 cup chopped fresh parsley
2 medium red onions, chopped	

Coat the steaks evenly with the salt, pepper and 1 tbsp of the rosemary. Heat the oil in a large non-stick sauté pan. Sear the steaks about 2 minutes each side. Remove and keep warm in the oven. Sauté the onion and garlic in 2 tbsp of the stock for about 2 minutes. Add the remaining rosemary and stock, the wine and 1 tbsp of parsley. Simmer about 10 minutes or until the liquid has reduced by half. Add the steaks and cover with liquid. Simmer steaks in the onion relish at least another 4 minutes, turning once. Remove steaks and put the relish on top. Garnish with the remaining parsley.

Good muscle tone and bone density are essential for a healthy older life.

Grilled New York Steak with Balsamic Vinegar and Fresh Herbs

SERVES 4

CALORIES PER SERVING: 393.4

FAT (G) PER SERVING: 21.6

My friend Alberto, who lives with his lovely wife, Monica, in Milan, said he would take me out to a fantastic restaurant for a steak experience. I was so impressed I asked about the key ingredients and created this version.

2 10-oz New York steaks	2 tbsp chopped fresh oregano
3 tbsp balsamic vinegar	1 tbsp chopped fresh rosemary
1/4 cup canola oil	1/2 tsp white OR black pepper
1/4 cup lemon juice	1 small red onion, finely
1 cup dry red wine	chopped

Trim fat from the steaks and cut each steak into 2. In a shallow baking dish, combine the balsamic vinegar, oil, lemon juice, wine, oregano, rosemary and pepper. Place the steaks in the marinade and refrigerate, covered, at least 1 hour, turning once. Remove steaks from marinade, reserving marinade. Grill or broil steaks to desired doneness. (Rare 5 minutes each side; medium 7–8 minutes each side; well done 12 minutes each side.) Meanwhile, in a saucepan, combine the marinade and onion. Bring to a boil, reduce heat and simmer for 5 minutes or until the sauce has reduced by half. Serve sauce on top of steak.

Substitution:
- *Replace New York steak with a cheaper cut, such as a 2-lb flank steak cut into 4. Marinate at least 4 hours to ensure tenderness.*

DESSERTS

Apple Cinnamon Upside-Down Cake

SERVES 8

CALORIES PER SERVING: 221.2

FAT (G) PER SERVING: 4.7

This is so delicious, you might want to serve this at breakfast or at brunch!

TOPPING:	1 tsp cinnamon
1 tbsp calorie-reduced margarine	1/2 tsp nutmeg
1 tbsp brown sugar	1/2 tsp salt
1 tsp cinnamon	2 large egg whites
3 large apples, peeled, cored, and	1 cup non-fat or skim milk
thinly sliced	1/2 cup apple juice concentrate
	2 tbsp canola oil
BATTER:	1 tbsp vanilla
2 cups all-purpose flour	1 tbsp liquid sweetener,
2 tsp baking powder	such as Sugar Twin

To prepare the topping, melt the margarine and spread over the bottom of an 8- x 10-inch cake pan. Combine the brown sugar and cinnamon; spread on top of the margarine. Arrange the apples on the brown sugar mixture.

To prepare the batter, in a large bowl, combine the flour, baking powder, cinnamon, nutmeg and salt. Add the egg whites, milk, oil, apple juice concentrate, vanilla and sweetener. Mix well. Pour the batter over apple slices. Bake at 350°F for 45 minutes or until toothpick inserted in centre comes out clean. Let cake cool in pan. When cooled, flip over onto serving plate.

Apple Cranberry Muffins

MAKES 2 DOZEN MUFFINS

CALORIES PER MUFFIN: 95

FAT (G) PER MUFFIN: 2.9

Although I do use frozen cranberries, you can always substitute fresh.

3 cups all-purpose flour	1/4 cup canola oil
2 tbsp baking powder	2 eggs
1/2 tsp salt	1 1/3 cups unsweetened apple juice
1/4 cup liquid sweetener, such as Sugar Twin	2 cups frozen unsweetened cranberries

In a large bowl, combine the flour, baking powder and salt. Add the sweetener, oil, eggs and apple juice, stirring just until mixed. Grind the cranberries in a blender and fold into the batter. Spoon into a non-stick muffin pan and bake at 375°F for 25 minutes or until golden brown.

> When lifting weights, focus on each muscle group and move very smoothly.

Banana Walnut Loaf

MAKES 2 LOAVES, 8 SLICES PER LOAF

CALORIES PER SLICE: 200.7

FAT (G) PER SLICE: 3.5

If you haven't got 3 ripe bananas, then 3 over-ripe bananas will do.

3 cups all-purpose flour	1 large egg
1 cup sugar	3 ripe bananas, mashed
2 tsp baking powder	2 tbsp canola oil
1/2 tsp baking soda	2 cups non-fat sour cream
1/2 tsp cinnamon	1/2 cup chopped walnuts

In a large bowl, combine the flour, sugar, baking powder, baking soda and cinnamon. Add the egg, bananas, oil, sour cream and walnuts; mix well. Turn into 2 loaf pans and bake at 350°F for 55 to 60 minutes or until brown.

Exercise enhances cardiovascular function, typically reduces high blood pressure and helps many people handle stress. Once you start exercising you'll actually feel better and want to exercise more.

Banana Cheesecake

SERVES 10

CALORIES PER SERVING: 223.8

FAT (G) PER SERVING: 8.6

This is a stand-out—it's definitely one of my favourites.

1 cup graham wafer crumbs	1 tsp vanilla
3 tbsp brown sugar	10 oz calorie-reduced cream cheese
3 tbsp calorie-reduced margarine	2 ripe bananas, chopped
1/2 cup all-purpose flour	1 large egg
1/4 cup granulated sugar	2/3 cup non-fat sour cream
1 tsp cornstarch	1/2 cup non-fat or skim milk

In a large bowl, blend together the crumbs, brown sugar and margarine. Press into an 8-inch square pan. In a separate bowl, combine the flour, sugar, cornstarch, vanilla, cream cheese, bananas, egg, sour cream and milk. Using an electric mixer, mix well at high speed. Pour mixture into the pan and bake at 350°F for 45 minutes or until toothpick inserted in centre comes out clean.

Always warm up at least 5 minutes before doing any physical activity.

Cinnamon Coffee Cake

SERVES 8

CALORIES PER SERVING: 192.5

FAT (G) PER SERVING: 4.3

This is another delicious, all-purpose cake! It goes well with break-fast, brunch, lunch, tea time or dinner.

BATTER:	TOPPING:
1 cup all-purpose flour	1/2 cup graham wafer crumbs
1/2 cup brown sugar	3 tbsp calorie-reduced margarine
2 tsp cinnamon	4 tsp brown sugar
1 tsp baking powder	1/2 tsp cinnamon
1/2 tsp baking soda	
2 eggs	
1 tsp vanilla	

To prepare the batter, in a medium bowl, combine the flour, brown sugar, cinnamon, baking powder, baking soda, eggs and vanilla; mix well. Pour into an 8-inch square cake pan. To prepare the topping, in a small bowl, combine the graham wafer crumbs, margarine, brown sugar and cinnamon; blend well. Swirl, with a spoon, on top of batter. Bake at 350°F for 45 to 50 minutes or until toothpick inserted in the centre comes out clean.

Make sure you have appropriate footwear for the activity of your choice.

Ken's Favourite Chocolate Cake

SERVES 12

CALORIES PER SERVING: 146.5

FAT (G) PER SERVING: 1.6

You know, I've tried a lot of chocolate cakes (my downfall) but this one always comes out on top (it could be the non-fat sour cream!).

1 cup all-purpose flour	1/2 cup non-fat or skim milk
1 cup low-fat cocoa	1 cup granulated sugar
2 large eggs	1 tsp baking powder
1 tbsp vanilla	1/2 tsp baking soda
1/2 cup non-fat sour cream	2 tbsp icing sugar

In a large bowl, combine the flour, cocoa, eggs, vanilla, sour cream, milk, granulated sugar, baking powder and baking soda; blend until smooth. Pour into a non-stick 8-inch square cake pan that has been sprayed with cooking spray. Bake at 350°F for about 50 minutes or until a toothpick inserted in the centre comes out clean. Turn out of pan and let cool. Sift icing sugar over top.

Exercise increases the skeleton's calcium absorption.

Low-Fat Raisin Biscotti

MAKES 18 TO 20 BISCOTTI

CALORIES PER BISCOTTI: 79.9 – 88.8

FAT (G) PER BISCOTTI: 2.4 – 2.7

Biscotti tastes great with coffee after dinner—don't be afraid to dunk it.

1-1/2 cups all-purpose flour	3 egg whites
1 tsp baking powder	1 tsp vanilla
Pinch salt	1/2 tsp cinnamon
1/2 cup unsalted butter	1/2 cup raisins
1/4 cup sugar	

In a large bowl, combine the flour, baking powder and salt; mix well. In a separate bowl, cream the butter and sugar. Add the egg whites, one at a time, beating well after each addition. Add the vanilla, cinnamon, flour mixture and raisins; mix until a rather firm dough forms. Divide dough in half. Using your hands, roll dough into 2 small logs and place on a wax-paper-lined cookie sheet. Bake at 350°F for 20 minutes or until light brown on top. Remove from oven and cool. Diagonally cut the log into 1/2-inch-thick slices. Return to cookie sheet and bake at 350°F for 5 minutes on each side or until crisp.

Low-Fat Orange Cookies

MAKES 3 DOZEN COOKIES

CALORIES PER COOKIE: 67.7

FAT (G) PER COOKIE: 0.4

These are so delicious and easy to make that they'll probably become part of your cookie repertoire!

3 cups all-purpose flour

1 cup quick-cooking rolled oats

1/2 cup sugar

3 tbsp baking powder

1 1/2 tsp nutmeg

1 tsp cinnamon

1/2 tsp salt

1 large egg, lightly beaten

1/2 cup non-fat or skim milk

1/2 cup non-fat sour cream

2 tbsp chopped orange zest

1 cup unsweetened orange juice
  (with pulp)

In a large bowl, combine the flour, oats, sugar, baking powder, nutmeg, cinnamon and salt; mix well. Add the egg, milk, sour cream, orange zest and orange juice; mix well. Roll a tablespoon of batter at a time into a ball and place on a non-stick cookie sheet. Flatten each slightly with finger. Bake at 375°F for about 15 minutes or until brown.

Add life to your years and years to your life by exercising regularly.

Peach Bread Pudding

SERVES 10

CALORIES PER SERVING: 234.7

FAT (G) PER SERVING: 3.3

This tastes as delicious as it sounds. (You can always replace the peaches with nectarines or apricots—just be aware the calorie count will vary slightly.)

2 cups non-fat or skim milk	1/2 tsp cinnamon
1/2 cup non-fat yogurt	6 cups day-old bread torn into
3 large eggs	small pieces
1/4 cup granulated sugar	3 cups chopped peaches
1/4 cup low-fat condensed milk	(about 6 medium)
1 tsp vanilla	

In a large bowl, combine the fat-free milk, yogurt, eggs, sugar, condensed milk, vanilla and cinnamon; mix well. In a separate bowl, combine the bread and peaches. Pour the wet mixture over the bread mixture and mix. Pour into a 7- x 11-inch non-stick baking dish and bake at 350°F for 50 minutes or until toothpick inserted in the centre comes out clean. Allow to cool prior to serving.

Exercise helps to slow bone loss in the menopause years and beyond.

Strawberry Yogurt Smoothie

SERVES 6 TO 8

CALORIES PER SERVING: 117.1 – 156.1

FAT (G) PER SERVING: 1.9 – 2.5

This smoothie is so tasty I often have this for breakfast.

2 cups non-fat yogurt
2 cups fresh strawberries
1/2 cup low-fat condensed milk
1/2 cup non-fat sour cream
1 tsp vanilla

In a blender or food processor, combine the yogurt, strawberries, condensed milk, sour cream and vanilla; blend until smooth. Place in 6 to 8 dessert dishes and chill for 2 hours. Garnish with a fresh strawberry.

Your heart needs more than love—it needs the benefit of exercise.

Banana Yogurt Smoothie

SERVES 6 TO 8

CALORIES PER SERVING: 131.4 – 175.1

FAT (G) PER SERVING: 1.9 – 2.5

Not only is this delicious, it's wonderfully filling!

2 cups non-fat yogurt	1/2 cup non-fat sour cream
2 ripe bananas, mashed	1 tsp vanilla
1/2 cup low-fat condensed milk	1/2 tsp cinnamon

In a blender or food processor, combine the yogurt, bananas, condensed milk, sour cream, vanilla and cinnamon; blend until smooth. Place in 6 to 8 dessert dishes and chill for 2 hours. Garnish with a light sprinkle of cinnamon.

Healthy abdominal muscles give added support to your internal organs.

Index

crouton salad, 30

cucumber

    and fennel salad, 32

    soup, chilled, 15

dessert

    biscotti, low-fat raisin, 164

    bread pudding, peach, 166

    cake, apple cinnamon upside-down, 158

    cake, chocolate, 163

    cake, cinnamon coffee, 162

    cheesecake, banana, 161

    cookies, low-fat orange, 165

    loaf, banana walnut, 160

    muffins, apple cranberry, 159

    yogurt, banana smoothie, 168

    yogurt, strawberry smoothie, 167

dressings *See* Salad Dressings

eggplant

    grilled, 56

    roasted, 99

fennel

    baked, 97

    and cucumber salad, 32

    and peppers, 54

    and shrimp salad, 40

fettuccine, 84

fish *See also* Seafood

    Mediterranean chowder, 27

    stew, 119

foods, healthful, 5–6

fruit

    apple cinnamon upside-down cake, 158

    apple cranberry muffins, 159

    apple, pear and nectarine, sautéed, 70

    banana cheesecake, 161

    banana walnut loaf, 160

    banana yogurt smoothie, 168

    ratatouille, tangy, 59

    rice with apples and raisins, 69

    strawberry yogurt smoothie, 167

    with vegetables and tofu, 102

fusilli

    with goat cheese, 87

    with turkey bacon, 88

garlic

    dill dressing, 45

    lemon dressing, 44

gazpacho soup, 13, 14

halibut

    baked with fennel, 108

    with vegetable relish, 108

honey and mustard sauce, 46

honeydew melon soup, 16

lamb

    chops, orange and garlic, 144

    Mediterranean stew, 143

    stew, with lemon and fennel, 142

lasagna,

    seafood, 90

    vegetable, 89

lentil and tomato soup, 20

macaroni, with cheese and ground

    chicken, 76

meat

    beef steak with rosemary and onion

        relish, 155

    beef stew with mushrooms and

        herbs, 153

    beef, stir-fried with ginger and

        broccoli, 151

    beef tenderloin, 154

    beef and tomato stew, 152

    lamb chops, orange and garlic, 144

Dear Ken,

I watch your show almost daily. I love all of your recipes and
have both of the cookbooks! I've been watching What's for
Dinner? for a couple of years now and I like all the changes to
the set. (I love the kitchen!) You guys are doing a great job.
Congratulations!...

Sincerely,

Deanna in Vancouver

If you'd like to write to Ken Kostick, please address your letters to:

Ken Kostick
Box 116
2255 Queen Street East
Toronto, Ontario
M4E 1G3